MODERN MATHEMATICS
VOLUME

General Editor
D. C. PAVATE, M.A. (Cantab)

MODERN
COLLEGE ALGEBRA

By

D. C. PAVATE, M.A. (Cantab)

Formerly Research Scholar, Sidney
Sussex College, Cambridge

LONDON
MACMILLAN & CO LTD
1967

First Edition 1966
Reprinted 1967 (*twice*)

Published by
MACMILLAN & CO LTD
Little Essex Street London WC 2
and also at Bombay Calcutta and Madras
Macmillan South Africa (Publishers) Pty Ltd Johannesburg
The Macmillan Company of Australia Pty Ltd Melbourne
The Macmillan Company of Canada Ltd Toronto
St Martin's Press Inc New York

MADE IN INDIA AT THE I.S.S.D. PRESS, MADRAS 2

PREFACE

This is the third book in the Modern Mathematical Series and is intended for the use of students doing the first year degree course, whether in Arts, Science or Engineering. This book is a sort of continuation of my 'Modern Algebra' for pre-university classes. The topics included in this book are of fundamental importance to all students of Mathematics at this stage, particularly to Engineering students. The material in the text is about the same as that usually done in these classes; but the treatment is more rigorous than is usually provided in texts meant for the first year class of the three-year degree courses or the Intermediate classes.

Recent efforts of logicians and students of the foundations of mathematics to clarify such fundamental concepts as set, number, order, relation, function, etc. have yielded powerful mathematical tools. Indeed they have made mathematics more enjoyable and easier to learn. Abstract thinking is the heart of mathematics. The first five chapters of the book are, therefore, mainly concerned with such basic concepts. During the last fifty years, matrices have come to occupy an important position in Mathematics. Apart from their intrinsic value as an intellectual exercise in Mathematics, they have vast applications to Modern Physics, Economics, Statistics, and several branches of Engineering.

It is usual now to teach matrices as early as possible. In several countries, they are taught at the higher stage of secondary schools, along with some other topics of Abstract Algebra. Hence matrices have been assigned an important place in this book although the treatment is quite elementary. It is usual now to treat determinants as an off-shoot of Matrices. The other topics dealt with such as the Euclid's Algorithm, Polynomial functions, equations and infinite series are such as can be taught profitably at this stage. It is desirable that at least at this stage, the students should know the logical proof of $(-a) \cdot (-b) = ab$. I have, therefore, dealt with the basic properties of the real number system by the use of certain postulates in the second chapter.

Before sending the manuscript of the book to the Press, I showed it to several members of the teaching staff of the Karnatak University. They have all made useful suggestions for improvement. My thanks are due, in this connection, to Dr. S. K. Singh, Dr. B. R. Bhat, Dr. E. Sampatkumarachar and my son Shri K. D. Pavate who originally drafted some of the chapters for me.

Karnatak University,   D. C. PAVATE.
    Dharwar,
  10th March, 1966.

CONTENTS

CHAPTER 1

The Language and Notation of Sets

1.1. The concept of a *set* is very important in modern Mathematics. The idea is not new, as it is widely used in every day life in the sense of *class* or *collection* or *aggregate*. For instance, we talk of a set of books in a library or a set of students in a class. A set is a collection of well-defined objects thought of as a whole. The objects must be precisely stated. These objects are spoken of as *elements* or members of the set. A set is made up of elements and the elements belong to or are members of the set. We generally denote sets by capital letters like A and elements by small letters like a. To denote that a is an element of the set A or ' a belongs to A ', we write $a \in A$. The symbol $\in$ (the Greek letter epsilon) is read ' is a member of ' or ' belongs to '. If a and b belong to A, we may write $a, b \in A$. For instance, 2 is a member of the set of all positive integers N (i.e. of natural numbers); we express this fact by writing $2 \in N$. Similarly, $\frac{1}{2}, \frac{3}{5} \in Q$, where Q is the set of all quotients of the type p/q, where p and q are any two integers and $q \neq o$. No attempt is necessary to define the terms—set and an element of a set. We may take them as primitive or undefined terms and then proceed to define other concepts in terms of them and to lay down as axioms the properties which are necessary. Set theory is relatively new, though basic in Mathematics. The German mathematician G. Cantor (1845–1918) was the originator of the theory.

There are two ways of describing a set: it can be listed or described by a property in braces. For instance, take the set A of the ten digits used in the decimal system.

$$A = \{0,\ 1,\ 2,\ 3,\ 4,\ 5,\ 6,\ 7,\ 8,\ 9\} \quad \text{or}$$
$$A = \{a \mid a \text{ is a digit}\}.$$

The vertical bar is read ' such that '.

In the first case we have listed all the ten digits and in the second case we have used the descriptive property of the elements. In many cases it may not be possible to list all the elements. For instance, the set of positive integers has an unlimited number of elements. Such a set is called an infinite set. Even in a set of finite number of elements, the number of elements may be too large to enumerate. In such cases, the use of a descriptive phrase in braces is more desirable. Suppose A is the set of English alphabets. This can be expressed as

$A = \{a,\ b,\ c,\ \ldots\ldots\ldots\ x,\ y,\ z\}$ which is somewhat troublesome, compared with $A = \{a \mid a$ is a letter in the English alphabet$\}$. The latter is neater too.

1.2. Subsets.

Consider sets A, B where $A = \{2,\ 3,\ 4\}$ and $B = \{1,\ 2,\ 3,\ 4,\ 5\}$. Here every element of A is an element of B, but every element of B is not an element of A. In such cases we say that A is a proper subset of B and denote the fact by the notation $A \subset B$. If A and B are sets with the property that every element of A is an element of B, A is said to be a subset of B and is written $A \subseteq B$. This means that A is contained in B. By this definition $A \subseteq A$ and hence every set is a subset of itself. In the example given above, however, A is a proper subset of B i.e. B is not a subset of A according to our definition. If $A \subseteq B$ and $B \subseteq A$, then A and B have exactly the same elements. In such cases, the two sets are said to be equal and we write $A = B$. When this is not the case and yet A is a subset of B, we call A a proper subset of B and indicate the fact by the notation $A \subset B$.

Definition: The set A is a subset of the set B, if every element of A is an element of B. If B has elements that are not elements of A, then A is a proper subset of B. In symbols $A \subset B$ if and only if $x \in A$ implies $x \in B$ and there exists an element in B which is not in A.

It is not absolutely necessary that a set should have elements. A set may have no elements. Such a set is called a *null set* or an *empty set* and is denoted by ϕ. For instance, the set of integers which are perfect squares and end in 7 is ϕ. By its very definition the empty set is a subset of every set.

1.3. Operation on sets.

Suppose there is an over-all set U, from which sets A, B, C are formed in any context. For instance U may be the set of positive integers i.e. $U = \{1, 2, 3, \ldots\}$ and $A = \{1, 2, 3, 4, 5\}$, $B = \{2, 3\}$, $C = \{3, 4, 5, 6\}$ etc. All these sets $A, B, C, \ldots$ are proper subsets of U. Here there are two special sets: U, the universal set which contains all these sets and the null set ϕ which has no element at all.

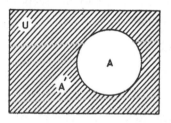

$\therefore \phi \subseteq A \subseteq U$ for any A.

If we form any set A out of U, the remaining elements of U will form another set A'. A and A' are spoken of as the *complements* of each other.

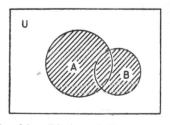

If A and B are any two sets, the union of A and B, denoted by $A \cup B$, is the set of those elements and only those elements which are in A *or* in B (or in both). If A and B are any two sets, the intersection of A and

B, denoted *A* ∩ *B* is the set of those elements and only those elements which are in *A and* in *B*. That is, *A* ∩ *B* is the set of elements that are in both *A* and *B*.

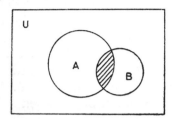

Consider $A = \{1,\ 2,\ 3,\ 4,\ 5\}$, $B = \{2,\ 3\}$ and $C = \{4,\ 5\}$. Now $A \cup B = A$ and $B \cup C = \{2,\ 3,\ 4,\ 5\}$. Also $A \cap B = B$, $B \cap C = \phi$.

These operations on sets can be illustrated by means of Venn diagrams. The universal set *U* is represented by points within a rectangle, and sets *A*, *B* .... are shown by points within circles drawn inside the rectangles.

1.4. Identical and equivalent sets.

Two sets are said to be identical if they have exactly the same members. Thus the sets

$A = \{a,\ b,\ c\}$ and $B = \{a,\ c,\ b\}$ are identical. The elements need not be written in the same order.

The sets $\{1,\ 3,\ 5\}$ and $\{2,\ 4,\ 5\}$ are not identical, as two members of the two sets are different. Here the sets are spoken of as being *equivalent* as the number of elements in each of them is the same. If the symbol $n\{A\}$ is defined to mean the number of elements in the set, then we may write,

$n\{a,\ b,\ c\} = 3$, $n\{a,\ b,\ c,\ d\} = 4$ etc.
If $A = \{a,\ b,\ c\}$ and $B = \{1,\ 2,\ 3\}$
  $n(A) = n(B)$.

Example: By using Venn diagrams, find $n(X)$, given $n(X \cup Y) = 25$, $n(X \cap Y) = 5$ and $n(Y) = 14$.

$n(X \cap Y) = 5$ means there are 5 elements common to X and Y. $n(X \cup Y)$ stands for the number of elements in $X \cup Y =$ the number of elements in $(Y) +$ the number of elements in X — the number of common elements

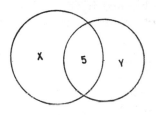

$$= 14 + n(X) - 5 = 25$$
$$\therefore n(X) = 16.$$

The operations of union and intersection need not be confined to two sets. The concept may be extended to any number of sets $A, B, C \ldots$. The *union* of $A, B, C \ldots$. is the set consisting of those elements which are in *at least one* of the given sets and the intersection of $A, B, C \ldots$. is the set consisting of those elements which are in *all* the given sets. $A \cup B$ can be also written $A + B$. The difference of two sets A and B is the set of all elements that belong to A but not to B. Thus $A - B = \{x \mid x \in A \text{ and } x \notin B\}$ with the usual notation.

1.5. The product set.

Sometimes the order of the elements in a set is significant. This may be illustrated by the familiar idea of coordinates (x, y) of a point in a plane. A pair of elements like (x, y) in which we distinguish one of the elements as the first and the other as the second is called an *ordered pair*. Note that (x, y) is different from (y, x) unless x and y happen to be equal real numbers.

If X and Y are any two sets, the set of all ordered pairs (x, y) of elements such that $x \in X$ and $y \in Y$ is called the product set of X and Y, and is denoted by $X \times Y$ or $X \cdot Y$. If the sets X and Y represent points on the x-axis and y-axis (as in Cartesian coordinate Geometry), $X \cdot Y$ represents all the points in the plane containing the two axes. In symbols,

$$X \cdot Y = \{(x, y) \mid x \in X \text{ and } y \in Y\}.$$

The set $X \cdot Y$ is sometimes called the Cartesian product.

Example 1: If $X=\{1, 2\}$ and $Y=\{1, 2, 3\}$ the set $X \cdot Y$ is obtained by the ordered pairs of one element of X and any one element of Y.

If we take 1 of X, it will give rise to three ordered pairs by taking any one of the elements of Y. Thus, (1, 1), (1, 2), (1, 3).

Similarly taking the element 2 of X, we have three more ordered pairs (2, 1), (2, 2), (2, 3). Thus there are 2×3 or 6 ordered pairs in all.

Example 2: If $X=\{a, b, c\}$ and $Y=\{1, 2, 3\}$ find the ordered pairs of the product set $X \cdot Y$.

For the element a of X, we have three ordered pairs $(a, 1)$ $(a, 2)$ and $(a, 3)$. Similarly for b of X, we have three ordered pairs $(b, 1)$, $(b, 2)$ and $(b, 3)$. Similarly for c of X, there are three more ordered pairs $(c, 1)$, $(c, 2)$ and $(c, 3)$. Thus there are 3×3 or 9 ordered pairs.

Note that X and Y may be identical sets. If $X=\{1, 2\}$ $X \cdot X=\{(1, 1), (1, 2), (2, 1), (2, 2)\}$.

Exercise

1. If $U=\{1, 2, 3, 4, 5\}$ and $A=\{1, 5\}$, find A'.

2. If $A=\{a, b, c\}$ and $B=\{a, 3, 5\}$ find $A \cup B$ and $A \cap B$.

3. If $A=\{1, 2\}$ find all the subsets of A, containing (i) two elements, (ii) one element and (iii) no element. How many subsets are there in all?

4. If $A=\{a, b, c\}$, list all the subsets containing 3, 2, 1 or no elements. How many subsets are there in all? Similarly show that there are 16 or 2^4 subsets of the set $\{a, b, c, d\}$. Find a general formula for the number of subsets of a set with n elements.

5. If N is the set of all positive integers, determine the subsets $A=\{a \mid a \in N, a < 5\}$, $B=\{a \mid a \in N, a \geqslant 5\}$. Find $A \cup B$ and $A \cap B$.

6. If $A=\{0, 1, 2, 3\}$, and $B=\{1, 2, 3\}$, how many ordered pairs are there in (i) $A \cdot B$, (ii) $B \cdot A$, (iii) $A \cdot A$?

7. If $A=\{-3, 2, 4\}$, determine the set $A \cdot A$.

8. By considering the sets $X = \{1, 2\}$ and $Y=\{a, b, c\}$, show that $X \cdot Y \neq Y \cdot X$.

9. Show by using Venn diagram that $B \subset A$ if and only if $A' \subset B'$.

10. State the conditions in which the sets A and B would have the following relations:

   (i) $A \cap B = \phi$ (ii) $A \cup B = \phi$

  (iii) $A \cap B = U$ (iv) $A \cup B = U$

   (v) $A \cup U = U$ (vi) $A \cup \phi = \phi$

Which of the following statements are true for sets A, B, C?

11. $A \subset A \cup B$.

12. $A \subset A \cap B$.

13. $A \cap (B-A) = \phi$.

14. $A-B \subset A$.

15. If $A = A \cup B$, then $B \subset A$.

16. If $A \subset B$ and $B \subset C$, then $A \subset C$.

17. $(A-B) \cap (A-C) = A-(B \cup C)$.

18. $(A-B) \cap (A \cup B) = A \cap B$.

19. If $n(A \cup B)=32$, $n(A \cap B)=7$ and $n(A)=10$, find $n(B)$. Use Venn diagrams.

20. If $n(A \cup B)=24$, $n(A)=17$ and $n(B)=11$, find $n(A \cap B)$ and $n(A)-n(B)$.

CHAPTER 2

Real Numbers

2.1. The set of real numbers R. The set of all decimals (periodic and non-periodic) represents a set of numbers which is called the *set of real numbers*. The real numbers include rational numbers like $\frac{2}{1}$, $\frac{3}{4}$, $\frac{7}{5}$, $\frac{1}{3}$ (or 2, ·75, 1·4, ·3333 ....) and irrational numbers like $\sqrt{2}$, $\sqrt[3]{2}$, π (or 1·414...., 1·259...., 3·14159,....). A rational number may be represented by either a terminating or a non-terminating recurring decimal, while an irrational number is just a non-recurring infinite decimal. There is, however, a definite point corresponding to each finite or infinite decimal. We, therefore, think of real numbers as being arranged as points on a number-line like this:

The set of real numbers R contains all the rational numbers and integers as subsets. With the usual notation,

N stands for the set of natural numbers (1, 2, 3, 4, ...),

I ,,   ,,   ,,   integers (.... −3, −2, −1, 0, 1, 2, 3, ...),

Q ,,   ,,   ,,   quotients or rational numbers.

N is a subset of I and I is a subset of Q, for, the number 3 is the quotient $\frac{3}{1}$ which is a rational number.

$$\therefore N \subset I \subset Q \subset R.$$

2.2. Instead of trying to define what the real numbers are, we may start by assuming that the real numbers, whatever

16

they are, satisfy certain basic algebraic laws. These basic laws or assumptions are called *postulates* for the real numbers. We start with two operations, addition and multiplication; subtraction and division follow from them. Thus we deal with the set R of real numbers and the two operations $+$ and $\times$ (or $\cdot$). The algebraic structure we are dealing with is a triplet $[R, +, \cdot]$. The product $a \cdot b$ is often denoted simply as ab, while dealing with letters as numbers.

Postulates:

(1) **Closure:** R is closed under addition and multiplication. That is, if a and $b \in R$, then $a+b$ and $a \cdot b \in R$.

(2) **Commutative Laws:** For all a and b in R, $a+b=b+a$ and $ab=ba$.

(3) **Associative Laws:** For all a, b and c in R, $a+(b+c)=(a+b)+c$ and $a(bc)=(ab)c$.

(4) **Distributive Law:** For all a, b, and c in R, $a(b+c)=ab+ac$.

(5) **Zero:** R contains a unique element 0 such that $a+0=a$, for all a in R.

Since the sum of zero and any real number is that number itself, zero is called the *identity* or *neutral* element for addition.

(6) **Unity:** R contains an element 1 (which is different from zero) such that $a \cdot 1 = a$ for all a in R. This is called the identity element for multiplication.

(7) **Additive inverse:** For each a in R, there is exactly one number $-a$ in R, called the negative of a, such that $a+(-a)=(-a)+a=0$.

(8) **Multiplicative inverse:** For every a in R, other than 0, there is exactly one number $a^{-1}\left(\text{or } \dfrac{1}{a}\right)$, called the reciprocal of a, such that $a \cdot a^{-1}=a^{-1} \cdot a=1$.

(9) **Uniqueness:** If $a=b$ and $c=d$ in R, then $a+c=b+d$ and $ac=bd$. This law merely states that the sum or multiplication of two numbers depends only on the numbers and does not depend on the symbols we use to denote the numbers. Subtraction is defined by means of the negative given by the additive inverse in (7) above. That is,

$$a-b=a+(-b).$$

Similarly division is defined by the Multiplicative inverse given in (8) above. That is, if $b \neq 0$

$$\frac{a}{b}=a \div b=ab^{-1}.$$

2.3. Consequences of the postulates.

From the Additive inverse (7) and the Multiplicative inverse (8), we obtain the usual cancellation rules.

(1) If $a+b=a+c$, then it follows that $b=c$.

Proof: $a+b=a+c$ (given).

Add $(-a)$ to both sides.

$$(-a)+(a+b)=(-a)+(a+c)$$

From the Associative law,

$$(-a)+(a+b)=[(-a)+a]+b=[a+(-a)]+b$$
$$=0+b \text{ by the Additive Inverse}$$
$$=b \text{ by the postulate (5) on Zero.}$$

Similarly $(-a)+(a+c)=[-a+(a)]+c=0+c=c$

$$\therefore \ b=c.$$

(2) If $a \cdot b=a \cdot c$ and $a \neq 0$, then $b=c$.

Proof: From postulate 8, a has a reciprocal a^{-1} such that $a \cdot a^{-1}=1$.

Given that $ab=ac$, $a \neq 0$.

Multiplying both sides by a^{-1},

$$a^{-1} (ab) =a^{-1} (ac).$$

From the Associative law,
$a^{-1}(ab) = (a^{-1} \cdot a) \cdot b$ and $(a^{-1})(ac) = (a^{-1} \cdot a) \cdot c$
$\therefore 1 \cdot b = 1 \cdot c$
$\qquad \therefore b = c,$

(3) Operations with zero.

(a) For every a, $a \cdot 0 = 0$.
$\qquad$ If $a, b \in R$,
$\qquad b + 0 = b$ (the postulate 5 on zero).
$\therefore ab = a(b+0) = ab + a \cdot 0$ by distributive law.
$\therefore a \cdot 0$ is the identity element for addition.
$\therefore a \cdot 0 = 0$

(b) Zero has no reciprocal. That is, there is no real number a such that $a \cdot 0 = 1$.

From (a) above, $a \cdot 0 = 0$.
If there is a reciprocal a such that $a \cdot 0 = 1$,
$\qquad$ then $1 = 0$.
But by the postulate on unity, $1 \neq 0$.
$\therefore$ zero has no reciprocal.

(c) If $ab = 0$, then either $a = 0$ or $b = 0$. Suppose that a is not zero.
Then $ab = 0 = a \cdot 0$
By the cancellation law, we can cancel a from both sides.
$\qquad \therefore b = 0$

(4) Multiplication by negative.

(i) For every a, $-(-a) = a$.
According to the postulate on the additive inverse,
$\qquad -(-a)$ is a number x such that
$\qquad (-a) + x = x + (-a) = 0 \ldots \ldots (1)$
The number a has this property as $a + (-a) = 0 \ldots . (2)$
The postulate also tells us that every real number has exactly one negative. Hence x is unique.
$\therefore x = -(-a) = a$ comparing (1) and (2) above.

(ii) For every a and b, $(-a)b = -(ab) = a(-b)$.
By distributive law,

$$(-a)b+ab = [(-a)+a]b$$
$$= 0 \cdot b$$
$$= 0.$$

$\therefore (-a)b = -ab$ by the definition of a negative number.
Similarly $a(-b) = -ab$.

Thus we have proved that the product of a negative real number and a positive real number is negative.

(iii) For every a and b, $(-a)(-b) = ab$.

$$(-a)(-b) = -[a(-b)] \text{ by definition of subtraction}$$
$$= -[(-b)a] \text{ by commutative law.}$$
$$= -[-ba] \text{ by (ii) above.}$$
$$= ba \text{ by (i) above.}$$
$$= ab \text{ by commutative law.}$$

Thus we have proved that the product of two negative numbers is positive, e.g. $(-2) \cdot (-\frac{3}{2}) = 3$.

(iv) For every $a \neq 0$, $b \neq 0$, $(ab)^{-1} = a^{-1} \cdot b^{-1}$.

$$(ab)(a^{-1} \cdot b^{-1}) = a[b(a^{-1} \cdot b^{-1})]$$
$$= a[b(b^{-1}a^{-1})] \quad \text{by Associative law.}$$
$$= a[(b\ b^{-1})a^{-1}]$$
$$= a[1 \cdot a^{-1}] \quad \text{by postulate 8.}$$
$$= a \cdot a^{-1} \quad \text{(Identity element)}$$
$$= 1 \quad \text{(Multiplicative inverse)}$$
$$\therefore (a^{-1}b^{-1}) = (ab)^{-1} = \frac{1}{ab}.$$

(v) For every a and b, $-(a+b) = (-a)+(-b)$

$$(a+b)+[(-a)+(-b)] = a+[b+(-a)+(-b)]$$
$$= a+[b+(-b)+(-a)]$$
$$= a+[0+(-a)]$$
$$= a+(-a)$$
$$= 0$$

$\therefore [(-a)+(-b)]$ is the negative of $a+b$.
$\therefore -(a+b) = (-a)+(-b)$

This rule states that the negative of the sum is the sum of the negatives.

(5) The theorem on expansion.

For every a, b and x, $(x+a)(x+b)=x^2+x(a+b)+ab$.

By distributive law,

$$\begin{aligned}
(x+a)(x+b) &= x(x+b)+a(x+b) \\
&= x \cdot x + x \cdot b + a \cdot x + ab \\
&= x^2 + x(b+a) + ab \\
&= x^2 + x(a+b) + ab \text{ (commutative law)}
\end{aligned}$$

Note that x^2 is simply a way of writing the product of x and x. We write 2 for $1+1$, 3 for $2+1$ etc.

These results show that with the nine postulates we have assumed at the beginning of this chapter, it is possible to build up the entire algebraic structure which you have already learnt in the school.

An algebraic structure satisfying these postulates is called a *field*. Note that the set of integers is not a field; for, the operation of division is not possible, if we confine ourselves to the set of integers. For instance, there is no reciprocal of 2 in the set of integers. The set of rational numbers is a *field*, for it satisfies all the nine postulates. For each element a ($\neq 0$) in the set Q of rational numbers, there is an inverse element a^{-1} such that $a \cdot a^{-1} = 1$.

For instance, $\frac{3}{4}$ and $\frac{4}{3}$ are reciprocals of each other. The field of rational numbers is the first of several fields that we come across in Mathematics. Then comes the field of real numbers and we shall meet other fields later on. The set of integers which satisfies all the postulates except (8) comes under the category of an *integral domain*.

2.4. Illustrative examples.

Example 1 : Show that $-b+(a+b)=a$.

By commutative law $a+b=b+a$.

$$\begin{aligned}
\therefore \quad -b+(a+b) &= -b+(b+a) && \text{Commutative law} \\
&= (-b+b)+a && \text{Associative law} \\
&= 0+a && \text{Additive inverse} \\
&= a && \text{Definition of zero.}
\end{aligned}$$

Example 2: Prove that $a(b-c)=ab-ac$.

$$a(b-c) = a[b+(-c)] \quad \text{Definition of subtraction}$$
$$= ab+a(-c) \quad \text{Distributive law.}$$
$$= ab-ac \qquad \qquad 4\text{(ii)}$$

Example 3: Show that $-0=0$.

If $0=x$, then -0 is $-x$ so that

$$x+(-x)=0 \quad \text{(Additive inverse)}$$
$$\therefore \ 0+(-0)=0$$
$$\therefore \ (-0)=0 \quad \text{(definition of zero).}$$

Example 4: Show that if a, b, c, d are elements in any field,

$$\frac{a}{b}=\frac{c}{d} \text{ if and only if } ad=bc.$$

Given $\dfrac{a}{b}=\dfrac{c}{d}$ or $ab^{-1} = cd^{-1}$.

$$\therefore \ ad = a(b^{-1} \cdot b)d \qquad \text{(Multiplicative identity and}$$
$$\qquad\qquad\qquad\qquad\qquad \text{definition of unity)}$$
$$= (a \cdot b^{-1}) \cdot (b \cdot d) \quad \text{(Associative law)}$$
$$= (c \cdot d^{-1}) \, (b \cdot d) \quad \text{(Hypothesis)}$$
$$= c \, (d^{-1} \cdot d)b \quad \text{(Associative law)}$$
$$= c \cdot b \qquad\qquad \text{(Multiplicative identity)}$$
$$= bc \qquad\qquad \text{(Commutative law)}$$

The converse is also easy to prove.

If $ad=bc$, then $\dfrac{a}{b}=ab^{-1} = b^{-1} a= b^{-1} \cdot a \cdot d \cdot d^{-1}$

$$= b^{-1} \cdot b \cdot c \cdot d^{-1} \quad \text{(Hypo-}$$
$$\qquad\qquad\qquad\qquad \text{thesis)}$$
$$= c \cdot d^{-1}$$
$$= \frac{c}{d}.$$

Exercise

Prove by stating precisely which of the postulates are used in each of the following statements:

1. $2+0=2.$

2. $0+(-a)=(-a).$

3. $1\cdot5=5.$

4. $1\cdot1=1.$

5. $-1\cdot2=-2.$

6. $2+(-2)=0.$

7. $5\cdot\dfrac{1}{5}=1.$

8. $(-2)\cdot\dfrac{1}{2}=-1.$

9. $\dfrac{1}{3}\cdot\dfrac{1}{\frac{1}{3}}=1.$

10. $\pi+(-\pi)=0.$

11. $\pi\left(-\dfrac{1}{\pi}\right)=-1.$

12. $x+y=x\cdot1+y\cdot1.$

13. $a+a=2a.$

14. $(-1)a=-(1\cdot a)=-a.$

15. $(-a)+(-a)=-2a.$

16. $(-a)\cdot(-a)=a^2.$

17. $-a(b-c)=-ab+ac.$

18. $(a+b)^2=a^2+2ab+b^2.$

19. $b\left(\dfrac{a}{b}\right)=a,\ b\neq0.$

20. $\dfrac{0}{a}=0,\ a\neq0.$

21. $\dfrac{a}{b}\cdot\dfrac{c}{d}=\dfrac{ac}{bd}\quad(b,\ d\neq0).$

$$\left[Hint:\ \frac{a}{b}\cdot\frac{c}{d}=ab^{-1}\cdot cd^{-1}\right.$$
$$=a(b^{-1}c)d^{-1}$$
$$=a(cb^{-1})\,d^{-1}$$
$$=ac\cdot b^{-1}d^{-1}$$
$$=\left.\frac{ac}{bd}\right].$$

22. $\dfrac{a}{b}=\dfrac{ax}{bx}\ (b,\ x\neq0).$

23. $\dfrac{a}{b}+\left(-\dfrac{a}{b}\right)=0.$

24. $\left(\dfrac{a}{b}\right)\left(\dfrac{b}{a}\right)=1,\ a,\ b\neq0.$

25. Show that $2-(3-5)$ and $(2-3)-5$ are not the same. Are $2\div(3\div5)$ and $(2\div3)\div5$ the same?

Are the operations ' $-$ ' and ' $\div$ ' associative in the set R? Are they commutative? Give examples.

CHAPTER 3

Inequalities and Absolute Values

3.1. The ordering of the real numbers.

An important aspect of the real numbers is the possibility of arranging them on a number line like this:

The real numbers have been arranged on this line in ascending manner from the left to the right. The relation $a>b$ is read 'a is greater than b' and the relation $a<b$ is read 'a is less than b.' Graphically when we say that the real numbers have been arranged in an ascending manner, we mean that their value increases from the left to the right. That is $a>b$ means graphically that a lies to the right of b and $a<b$ means that a lies to the left of b.

Definitions: 1. If a and $b \in R$, the relation $a<b$ holds if and only if the difference $b-a$ is a positive number;

2. $a<b$ means $b>a$;

3. a is *positive* if $a>0$ and negative if $a<0$.

For instance, $-4<1$, as $1-(-4)=1+4=5$, a positive number. $\therefore 1>-4$. Similarly $0>-2$ and <2. It follows from definition that 0 is neither positive nor negative.

3.2. The Basic Inequality Postulates.

If any field, such as the set of real numbers R, satisfies the following postulates, the field is said to be *ordered*.

Postulate 1: If a and $b \in R$, then one and only one of the following statements is true:

$a > b$, $a = b$, $a < b$.

This is known as the law of *trichotomy*.

Postulate 2: If a, b, and $c \in R$ such that $a > b$ and $b > c$, then $a > c$. This is known as the *transitive law*.

Postulate 3: If a, b and $c \in R$ such that $a > b$, then $a + c > b + c$ i.e. $c + a > c + b$.

This is known as the *addition law*.

Note that c may be positive or negative.

Postulate 4: If a, b and $c \in R$, such that $a > b$ and $c > 0$, then $ac > bc$. This is known as the *multiplication law*.

As a particular case, if $a > 0$, and $b > 0$, then $ab > 0$. From these postulates, we can deduce some important theorems.

Theorem 1: If a and $b \in R$,

(i) $a > b$ if and only if $-a < -b$;

(ii) $a < b$ if and only if $-a > -b$.

Proof: By the additive law

$a + c > b + c$ if $a > b$.

Put $c = [(-a) + (-b)]$

$\therefore a + [(-a) + (-b)] > b + [(-a) + (-b)]$

By Associative Law

$[a + (-a)] + (-b) > [b + (-b)] + (-a)$

$\quad 0 + (-b) > 0 + (-a)$

i.e. $(-b) > (-a)$ which means $-a < -b$.

By reversing the steps we can prove the converse.

The second result can also be proved on these lines.

Corollary: If $a > 0$, then $-a < 0$.

Theorem 2: $1 > 0$.

By the law of *trichotomy*,

$1 > 0$, $1 = 0$ or $1 < 0$

$1 \neq 0$ by postulate 6 Chap. 2.

If $1 < 0$, $-1 > 0$ by theorem 1 above.

Now by postulate 4, $(-1)(-1) > 0$. But $(-1)(-1)=1$.

$\therefore$ $1>0$. This contradicts our assumption.

$\therefore$ $1>0$ and $-1<0$ by the law of trichotomy.

As a result of this theorem, we are able to establish order relations between any pair of integers.

For instance, $2>1$ i.e. $1+1>1$,

since $1>0$, and $1+1>1+0$.

Similarly $3>2>1>0$ and so on.

Theorem 3 : If $a>b$ and $c<0$, then $ac<bc$.

[For instance, if $a=-3$, $b=-5$ and $c=-1$

$(-3)(-1)$ or $3<(-5)(-1)$ or 5.]

Since $c<0$, $-c>0$. Thm. 1.

By Multiplication law,

$a(-c) > b(-c)$ or $-ac > -bc$.

$\therefore$ $bc>ac$ or $ac<bc$ (Theorem 1 above).

Similarly we can prove that if $a<b$ and $c<0$, then $ac>bc$.

$\therefore$ an inequality is reversed if we multiply both sides by the same negative number.

Theorem 4 : If $a>b$, and $c>d$, then $a+c>b+d$.

By postulate 3: $a+c > b+c$ and

$b+c > b+d$

By postulate 2, $a+c > b+d$.

Theorem 5 : If a, b, c and d are positive numbers, $a>b$ and $c>d$, then $ac>bd$.

$a>b$, $\therefore$ $ac>bc$ (postulate 4)

$c>d$, $\therefore$ $bc>bd$,,

$\therefore$ $ac>bd$ (by Transitive law)

More generally, if $a_1 \geqslant b_1>0$, $a_2 \geqslant b_2>0$,.. $a_n \geqslant b_n>0$, then $a_1a_2a_3 \ldots . a_n \geqslant b_1b_2b_3 .. b_n$, the sign of equality holding if and only if $a_1=b_1$, $a_2=b_2 \ldots$

3.3. Illustrative examples.

Example 1 : If $a > b$, show that

$$a > \frac{a+b}{2} > b.$$

$2a = a + a > a + b$, as $a > b$ (postulate 3).

$\therefore a > \dfrac{a+b}{2}$, by multiplying both sides by $\frac{1}{2}$

(postulate 4)

Similarly $b + a > b + b$ or $2b$.

$\therefore \dfrac{b+a}{2} > b$.   Hence the result.

Example 2 : If $a > b$ and $ab > 0$, then $\dfrac{1}{a} < \dfrac{1}{b}$.

Since ab is positive its reciprocal $(ab)^{-1}$ is also positive.

$\therefore a \cdot \dfrac{1}{ab} > b \cdot \dfrac{1}{ab}$ (postulate 4).

$\therefore \left(a \cdot \dfrac{1}{a} \right) \cdot \dfrac{1}{b} > \left(b \cdot \dfrac{1}{b} \right) \cdot \dfrac{1}{a}$

By the definition of the reciprocal $a \cdot \dfrac{1}{a} = 1 = b \cdot \dfrac{1}{b}$

$\therefore \dfrac{1}{b} > \dfrac{1}{a}$ or $\dfrac{1}{a} < \dfrac{1}{b}$.

Example 3 : Prove that $a^2 \geqslant 0$ for any $a \in R$.

First, let us assume a to be a positive number i.e. > 0.
Then $a \cdot a$ or $a^2 > 0$ by postulate 4.

If a is negative and $= -p$ where p is a positive number,
$a \cdot a = (-p) \cdot (-p) = p^2 > 0$ by the above result.

If $a = 0$, $0 \cdot 0 = 0$.

The sign of equality holds good only in case $a = 0$.
Otherwise, $a^2 > 0$.

Example 4: If $a>b$ and $c>d$, then $a-d>b-c$.

Since $c>d$, $-c<-d$ (Thm. 1)

$\therefore -d>-c$ (Defn.)

$\therefore a-d>b-c$ by applying theorem 4.

Example 5: If $a>b>0$ and $c>d>0$, then $\dfrac{a}{d}>\dfrac{b}{c}$.

Since $c>d$, $\dfrac{1}{c}<\dfrac{1}{d}$ from ex. 2 above.

$\therefore \dfrac{1}{d}>\dfrac{1}{c}$

By theorem 5, $a \cdot \dfrac{1}{d}>b \cdot \dfrac{1}{c}$ or $\dfrac{a}{d}>\dfrac{b}{c}$.

Exercise 3·1

1. If $a > b$ and $c > 0$, prove that $a+c > b$.

2. If $a > b$ and $c < 0$, prove that $a > b+c$.

3. If $a > 0$, prove that $-a < 0$ and if $a < 0$, prove that $-a > 0$.

4. If $a > 1$, show that $a^2 > a$ and if $a > 0$ but <1, prove that $a^2 < a$.

5. If $a > 1$, prove that $a^3 < a^5$.

6. Prove that (i) the sum of two positive real numbers is positive and (ii) the sum of two negative real numbers is negative.

7. Prove that the product ab is positive if and only if a and b are both positive or both negative.

8. Prove that the product ab is negative if and only if a is positive and b is negative or the other way round.

9. If $a > b > 0$ and n is a positive integer, prove that $a^n > b^n$. What happens if both a and b are negative?

10. Prove that if n is any positive integer and a and b are positive and $a^n > b^n$, then $a > b$. [Use the *trichotomy* postulate.]

11. If $a_1 \geqslant b_1, a_2 \geqslant b_2, \ldots\ldots a_n \geqslant b_n>0$, then
$a_1+a_2+ \ldots\ldots +a_n \geqslant b_1+b_2+ \ldots\ldots +b_n$ and
$a_1a_2a_3 \ldots\ldots a_n \geqslant b_1 b_2 b_3 \ldots b_n$.

Prove the following inequalities.

12. $a+b > \dfrac{2ab}{a+b}$ for any a and b such that $a+b > 0$.

13. $x + \dfrac{1}{x} \geqslant 2$ for any positive x.

14. $\dfrac{a}{b} + \dfrac{b}{a} > 2$ if $a \neq b$, $a > 0$, $b > 0$.

15. $a^3 + 3ab^2 > b^3 + 3a^2b$ if $a > b$ and $a \neq b$.

16. $a^3 + b^3 > a^2b + ab^2$ if $a \neq b$ and $a+b > 0$.

17. Show that if $\dfrac{a}{b} \leqslant \dfrac{c}{d}$, then $\dfrac{a+b}{b} \leqslant \dfrac{c+d}{d}$ and the sign of equality holds if and only if $ad = bc$.

18. Show that if $\dfrac{a}{b} \leqslant \dfrac{c}{d}$, then $\dfrac{a}{a+b} \leqslant \dfrac{c}{c+d}$ and that the sign of equality holds if and only if $ad = bc$.

19. $a^2 + b^2 + c^2 \geqslant ab + bc + ca$ for all a, b, c.   [*Hint:* $\Sigma(a-b)^2 \geqslant 0$.]

20. If a, b, c are positive numbers, $a^2b + b^2c + c^2a + ab^2 + bc^2 + ca^2 \geqslant 6abc$.

21. Prove that $(a^2 + b^2)(a^4 + b^4) \geqslant (a^3 + b^3)^2$ for all a and b such that $a + b \geqslant 0$.

22. Prove that $(a^2 + b^2)(c^2 + d^2) \geqslant (ac + bd)^2$ for all real a, b, c, d. (The Cauchy inequality).

3.4. Inequalities involving an unknown number.

Consider the inequality $3x - 10 < 7x + 2$, where x is any unknown real number.

By adding $10 - 3x$ to each side, $0 < 7x + 2 + 10 - 3x$ or $0 < 4x + 12$ (Addition Postulate).

$\therefore 4x + 12 > 0$ or $4x > -12$, by adding -12 to both sides. $\therefore x > -3$ by dividing both sides by 4 or multiplying both sides by $\frac{1}{4}$ (multiplication postulate). x here has many values, unlike the x in a simple equation. We speak of a solution set for equations (or open sentences) with the inequality sign.

Here the solution set consists of all real numbers greater than -3. i.e. $\{x \mid x > -3\}$.

For instance, $x = -2 \cdot 5$, 0, 2 are solutions.

Illustrative examples.

Example 1 : Find the solution set for $2x - 1 \leqslant \dfrac{8 - x}{2}$.

Multiplying both sides by 2, we have
 $4x - 2 \leqslant 8 - x$ $\therefore 5x \leqslant 10$ by adding $x + 2$ to both sides.
 $\therefore x \leqslant 2$. The sign of equality holds only when $x = 2$.
 $\therefore$ solution set can be expressed in the form
 $\left\{ x \mid 2x - 1 \leqslant \dfrac{8 - x}{2} \right\} = \{x \mid x \leqslant 2\}$. For instance, 0 is
 a solution.

Example 2 : Find the solution set for $x^2 + x - 12 > 0$.
 $x^2 + x - 12 > 0$ is the same thing as $(x + 4)(x - 3) > 0$
 This is possible for all values of $x > 3$ and < -4.
 Verify, for instance, for $x = -5$ and $x = 4$.
 $(-5)^2 - 5 - 12 = 8 > 0$ and $16 + 4 - 12 = 8$.
 $\therefore$ solution set is the set of all real numbers except the
 subset $\{-4 \leqslant x \leqslant 3\}$.

Exercise 3·2

Solve the following inequalities for x:

1. $3x + 9 \geqslant 0$.   **2.** $5x + 7 \leqslant x - 1$.

3. $3x - 9 \leqslant 0$.   **4.** $4x - 1 \leqslant x + 8$.

5. $7x - 2 \geqslant x + 10$.   **6.** $2x + \frac{1}{3} > 2 - 3x$.

7. $5x - 3 < 17x + 1$.   **8.** $\dfrac{x + 5}{2} > \dfrac{x - 2}{4}$.

9. $\dfrac{1}{3}x + \dfrac{1}{2} > \dfrac{x}{2} + \dfrac{1}{3}$. **10.** $\dfrac{5x}{8} - 1 \leqslant \dfrac{3x}{2} + \dfrac{9}{5}$.

11. $x^2 > 4$.   **12.** $4x^2 \leqslant 9$.

13. $(x-3)(x-4) > 0.$ **14.** $(x-2)(x-3) \leqslant 0.$

15. $(x-1)(x+3) > 0.$ **16.** $(x-2)(x+3) < 0.$

17. $x^2-3x+2 \leqslant 0.$ **18.** $x^2-5x-84 \geqslant 0.$

19. $(x+1)(x-3)(x-4) < 0.$

20. $(x-1)(x+3)(x+4) \geqslant 0.$

3.5. Powers and roots.

Definition: Any real number x whose nth power is a, that is, which satisfies the equation $x^n = a$, is called an nth root of a. Here n is any positive integer. In general, we shall see later that every number except zero has n distinct nth roots. The *principal* nth *root* of a positive number is the positive real root. Thus $x^2 = 4$ gives two roots $x = 2, -2$. The principal root is 2. The principal cube root of 27 is 3. The other two roots are imaginary (i.e. complex) numbers. If the number is negative and n is odd, the principal n^{th} root is the negative real root. Thus $x^3 + 8 = 0$ or $x^3 = -8$ gives $x = -2$ as the principal cube root of -8. But for $x^4 + 16 = 0$ or $x^4 = -16$, there is no real number whose 4th power is -16. Hence if n is even and the number is negative, there is no principal nth root. The symbol $\sqrt[n]{a}$ means the principal nth root. $\sqrt[2]{a}$ is also written $\sqrt{a}$; but higher roots like the third and fourth roots are written $\sqrt[3]{a}$ and $\sqrt[4]{a}$. We are now in a position to define $a^{\frac{p}{q}}$ where p and q are two positive integers without any common factor.

The symbol $a^{\frac{1}{q}}$ is defined as the principal qth root of a.

Hence $\sqrt[q]{a}$ is the same thing as $a^{\frac{1}{q}}$. Now

$$a^{\frac{1}{q}} \cdot a^{\frac{1}{q}} \;\ldots\ldots\; a^{\frac{1}{q}} \;(p \text{ factors of } a^{\frac{1}{q}}) = a^{p/q} .$$

Also $a^{\frac{p}{q}} \cdot a^{\frac{p}{q}} \cdot a^{\frac{p}{q}} \ldots \ldots a^{\frac{p}{q}}$ (q factors of $a^{\frac{p}{q}}$) $= a^p$

$\therefore \quad a^{\frac{p}{q}} = (a^p)^{\frac{1}{q}} = \left(a^{\frac{1}{q}}\right)^p = \sqrt[q]{a^p}$

From this discussion it follows that if $a > 0$, there exists a unique real number such that $a^{\frac{1}{n}} > 0$, where n is any integer. If $a > b > 0$, then $a^{\frac{1}{n}} > b^{\frac{1}{n}}$. For

$(a^{\frac{1}{n}}) \, (a^{\frac{1}{n}}) \, (a^{\frac{1}{n}}) \, \ldots \ldots n$ factors $= a$

$(b^{\frac{1}{n}}) \, (b^{\frac{1}{n}}) \, (b^{\frac{1}{n}}) \, \ldots \ldots \quad ,, \quad = b$

Since $a > b$, each of the n factors $a^{\frac{1}{n}}$ and $b^{\frac{1}{n}}$ must have the same relation. $\therefore a^{\frac{1}{n}} > b^{\frac{1}{n}}$. Here n is a positive integer. If m is another positive integer, we can show that $a^{\frac{m}{n}} > b^{\frac{m}{n}}$.

For, $(a^{\frac{1}{n}}) \, (a^{\frac{1}{n}}) \, \ldots \ldots$ to m factors is $a^{\frac{m}{n}}$ and

$(b^{\frac{1}{n}}) \, (b^{\frac{1}{n}}) \, \ldots \ldots$ to m factors is $b^{\frac{m}{n}}$.

$\therefore a^{\frac{m}{n}} > b^{\frac{m}{n}}$, as $a^{\frac{1}{n}} > b^{\frac{1}{n}}$.

If m is a negative integer equal $-p$ where p is a positive integer, we have

$a^{\frac{p}{n}} > b^{\frac{p}{n}} \qquad \therefore \qquad \dfrac{1}{a^{\frac{p}{n}}} < \dfrac{1}{b^{\frac{p}{n}}} \quad$ (see ex. 2 of 3.3.)

$\therefore \quad -\dfrac{p}{a^n} < -\dfrac{p}{b^n} \quad$ or $\quad b^{\frac{m}{n}} > a^{\frac{m}{n}}$.

In particular if $a > b$,

$\sqrt{a} > \sqrt{b} \quad$ and $\quad \dfrac{1}{\sqrt{a}} < \dfrac{1}{\sqrt{b}}$.

For instance, $25 < 29 < 36$ $\therefore$ $5 < \sqrt{29} < 6$

and $\dfrac{1}{5} > \dfrac{1}{\sqrt{29}} > \dfrac{1}{6}$.

Illustrative examples.

Example 6: For all a, b, prove that $\dfrac{a+b}{2} \leqslant \left(\dfrac{a^2+b^2}{2}\right)^{\frac{1}{2}}$.

This is proved if $\left(\dfrac{a+b}{2}\right)^2 \leqslant \left(\dfrac{a^2+b^2}{2}\right)$

or if $\dfrac{a^2+b^2+2ab}{4} \leqslant \dfrac{a^2+b^2}{2}$ or $a^2+b^2+2ab \leqslant 2(a^2+b^2)$

or $0 \leqslant a^2+b^2-2ab$ i.e. $0 \leqslant (a-b)^2$.

This is true as $(a-b)^2 \geqslant 0$.

$\therefore \dfrac{a+b}{2} \leqslant \left(\dfrac{a^2+b^2}{2}\right)^{\frac{1}{2}}$

Example 7: Prove that $\sqrt{3}+\sqrt{17} > \sqrt{7}+\sqrt{10}$

Assuming this to be true and squaring both sides,

$20+2\sqrt{51} > 17+2\sqrt{70}$ .... (1)

$\therefore 3+2\sqrt{51} > 2\sqrt{70}$

Squaring this again,

$9+204+12\sqrt{51} > 280$ .... (2)

i.e. $12\sqrt{51} > 280-213$ or 67

Squaring again

$144 \times 51 > 67 \times 67$

i.e. $7344 > 4489$ .... (3)

Now the result (3) is true. Putting $a = 7344$ and

$b = 4489$, $a > b$ $\therefore a^{\frac{1}{8}} > b^{\frac{1}{8}}$

Reversing the steps, we have

$\sqrt{3}+\sqrt{17} > \sqrt{7}+\sqrt{10}$

Example 8: If A is the Arithmetic mean and G is the Geometric mean of any two real numbers a and b, prove that $A \geqslant G$, provided $a > 0$, $b > 0$.

$$A = \frac{a+b}{2} \text{ and } G = \sqrt{ab}.$$

$$A - G = \frac{a+b}{2} - \sqrt{ab} = \frac{a+b-2\sqrt{ab}}{2}$$

$$= \frac{(\sqrt{a} - \sqrt{b})^2}{2}$$

$$\geqslant 0.$$

The equality sign holds good only in the case of $a = b$. If $a \neq b$, then $A > G$. The Arithmetic mean A of three positive numbers a, b, c, is $\dfrac{a+b+c}{3}$ and the Geometric mean is $\sqrt[3]{abc}$. The result $A > G$ holds good even in this case. That is,

$$\frac{a+b+c}{3} > \sqrt[3]{abc}$$

Here a, b, c, are positive numbers.
To remove the cube roots, put $a = x^3$, $b = y^3$, $c = z^3$ so that $x = a^{\frac{1}{3}}$, $y = b^{\frac{1}{3}}$, and $z = c^{\frac{1}{3}}$.

Now we have to prove that $\dfrac{x^3 + y^3 + z^3}{3} \geqslant xyz$

$$\begin{aligned}
x^3 + y^3 + z^3 - 3xyz &= (x+y+z)(x^2+y^2+z^2-xy-yz-zx) \\
&= \tfrac{1}{2}(x+y+z)\{(x-y)^2+(y-z)^2+(z-x)^2\} \\
&= \tfrac{1}{2}(x+y+z)\, \Sigma\,(x-y)^2 \\
&\geqslant 0 \text{ since } (x-y)^2 \text{ etc is } \geqslant 0 \text{ and } x+y+z \geqslant 0.
\end{aligned}$$

The sign of equality holds good only if $x = y = z$. Since a, b, c, are not equal, $\Sigma\,(x-y)^2 > 0$ and $x+y+z > 0$.

$$\therefore\ x^3 + y^3 + z^3 - 3xyz > 0$$
$$\text{or } x^3 + y^3 + x^3 > 3xyz.$$

$$\therefore\ a+b+c > 3\sqrt[3]{abc} \ \text{ or } \ \frac{a+b+c}{3} > \sqrt[3]{abc}.$$

We can prove the result even if there are four numbers, a_1, a_2, a_3, a_4. That is, $\dfrac{a_1+a_2+a_3+a_4}{4} \geqslant \sqrt[4]{a_1 a_2 a_3 a_4}$

Let $a = \dfrac{a_1+a_2}{2}$ and $b = \dfrac{a_3+a_4}{2}$ where a_1, a_2, a_3, a_4 are different positive numbers.

Since $\dfrac{a + b}{2} \geqslant \sqrt{ab}$,

$$\dfrac{\dfrac{a_1+a_2}{2} + \dfrac{a_3+a_4}{2}}{2} \geqslant \sqrt{\left(\dfrac{a_1+a_2}{2}\right)\left(\dfrac{a_3+a_4}{2}\right)}$$

or $\dfrac{a_1+a_2+a_3+a_4}{4} \geqslant \sqrt{\left(\dfrac{a_1+a_2}{2}\right)\left(\dfrac{a_3+a_4}{2}\right)}$

But $\dfrac{a_1+a_2}{2} \geqslant \sqrt{a_1 a_2}$ and $\dfrac{a_3+a_4}{2} \geqslant \sqrt{a_3 a_4}$

$\therefore \dfrac{a_1+a_2+a_3+a_4}{4} \geqslant \sqrt{(\sqrt{a_1 a_2})(\sqrt{a_3 a_4})}$ or $\sqrt[4]{a_1 a_2 a_3 a_4}$

Generally the arithmetic-mean and geometric-mean inequality has the form

$$\dfrac{a_1+a_2+a_3 \ldots + a_n}{n} \geqslant (a_1 a_2 a_3 \ldots a_n)^{\frac{1}{n}}$$

the equality sign holding good if and only if

$$a_1 = a_2 = a_3 \ldots = a_n.$$

Example 9 : Prove that $2\sqrt{n+1} - 2\sqrt{n} < \dfrac{1}{\sqrt{n}} < 2\sqrt{n} - 2\sqrt{n-1}$ where n is any positive integer.

Since $n+1 > n$, $\sqrt{n+1} > \sqrt{n}$.

$\therefore \dfrac{\sqrt{n+1}+\sqrt{n}}{2} > \sqrt{n}$ or $\dfrac{2}{\sqrt{n+1}+\sqrt{n}} < \dfrac{1}{\sqrt{n}}$.

Now $\dfrac{1}{\sqrt{n+1}+\sqrt{n}} = \dfrac{\sqrt{n+1}-\sqrt{n}}{\{\sqrt{(n+1)}+\sqrt{n}\}\{\sqrt{n+1}-\sqrt{n}\}}$

$\qquad\qquad\qquad\quad = \sqrt{n+1}-\sqrt{n}$

$\therefore\ 2\sqrt{n+1}-2\sqrt{n} < \dfrac{1}{\sqrt{n}}$ ...... (1)

Similarly $n-1 < n$ so that $\sqrt{n}+\sqrt{n-1} < 2\sqrt{n}$

$\therefore\ \dfrac{\sqrt{n}+\sqrt{n-1}}{2} < \sqrt{n}$

$\therefore\ \dfrac{2}{\sqrt{n}+\sqrt{n-1}} > \dfrac{1}{\sqrt{n}}$ or $2(\sqrt{n}-\sqrt{n-1}) > \dfrac{1}{\sqrt{n}}$

$\therefore\ \dfrac{1}{\sqrt{n}} < 2(\sqrt{n}-\sqrt{n-1})$ ...... (2)

$\therefore$ (1) and (2) provide the required result.

This is useful to prove that the sum of the series

$\dfrac{1}{\sqrt{1}}+\dfrac{1}{\sqrt{2}}+\dfrac{1}{\sqrt{3}}+...$ up to n terms lies between certain limits.

Let $n=100$, for instance.

The last term is $\dfrac{1}{\sqrt{100}}$ or $\dfrac{1}{10}$

By writing down the results of example 9 for different values of n we have

$2\sqrt{2}-2 \qquad <1 \quad =1$

$2\sqrt{3}-2\sqrt{2} < \dfrac{1}{\sqrt{2}} < 2\sqrt{2}-2$

$2\sqrt{4}-2\sqrt{3} < \dfrac{1}{\sqrt{3}} < 2\sqrt{3}-2\sqrt{2}$

$\qquad .. \qquad .. \qquad .. \qquad\qquad ..$

$\{2\sqrt{101}-2\sqrt{100}\} < \dfrac{1}{\sqrt{100}} < \{2\sqrt{100}-2\sqrt{99}\}$

Add: $2\sqrt{101}-2 < S < 2\times10-2+1$

where S is the sum $1+\dfrac{1}{\sqrt{2}}+\dfrac{1}{\sqrt{3}}+\ldots\ldots+\dfrac{1}{\sqrt{100}}$.

Since $\sqrt{101} > 10$, we have $S > 2\sqrt{101}-2$ or > 18 and $S < 20-1$ or $S > 18$ and < 19.

In the first line of inequalities above we write 1 instead of 2, which is obviously correct. This enables us to obtain 19 as the one limit instead of 20.

Exercise 3.3

Prove the following inequalities:

1. $2+2\sqrt{3} > 5$.

2. $2+\sqrt{7} < 5$.

3. $\sqrt{13}-2 > 1$.

4. $1+\sqrt[3]{7} < 3$.

5. $\sqrt[3]{5} < \sqrt{3}$.

6. $2\sqrt{7}-2\sqrt{6} < \dfrac{1}{\sqrt{6}}$.

7. $\dfrac{a}{b}+\dfrac{b}{a} \geqslant 2$ for any positive a, b.

8. Show that the harmonic mean of two positive numbers a and b is less than their geometric mean.

9. Show that for positive number $a_1, a_2, \ldots\ldots a_8$

$$\frac{a_1+a_2+\ldots\ldots+a_8}{8} \geqslant (a_1a_2a_3 \ldots a_8)^{\frac{1}{8}}$$

10. Prove that $\dfrac{x^2}{1+x^4} \leqslant \frac{1}{2}$ for any real value of x.

11. Which is the greater number $\sqrt{2}+\sqrt{6}$ or $\sqrt{3}+\sqrt{5}$?

12. Which is the greater number $\sqrt{\frac{4}{9}}+\sqrt{\frac{2}{5}}$ or $\sqrt{\frac{1}{3}}+\sqrt{\frac{2}{7}}$?

3.6. Absolute values.

The absolute value of a real number x indicates its size or magnitude without taking into considerations its sign. It is denoted by $|x|$. For example, $|-3| = |3| = 3$.

Definition: The absolute value of a real number x is defined by the following two conditions:

(1) $|x| = x$ if $x \geqslant 0$

(2) $|x| = -x$ if $x < 0$.

Theorem 6: For every x, $|x| \geqslant 0$.

From the two conditions above, if $x \geqslant 0$, then $|x| = x \geqslant 0$ and if $x < 0$, then $-x > 0$ $\therefore |x| = -x > 0$.

$\therefore |x| \geqslant 0$ in either case.

Theorem 7: For every x, $|-x| = |x|$.

If $x < 0$, then $-x > 0$ $\therefore |x| = -x$ by the second condition and $|-x| = -x$ by the first condition.

$\therefore |-x| = |x|$

If $x > 0$, then $-x < 0$; $|-x| = -(-x)$ by (2)
$= x = |x|$ by (1)

If $x = 0$, $|-x| = |x| = x = 0$ $\therefore |-x| = |x|$ in all cases.

Theorem 8: For every x, $|x| \geqslant x$.

If $x \geqslant 0$, $|x| = x$ and if $x < 0$, then $|x| = -x$, by the two conditions. In the second case, $|x| > x$ as $-x$ is positive and $> x$.

$\therefore |x| \geqslant x$ in either case.

The result can be expressed in the form $-|x| \leqslant x \leqslant |x|$.

Theorem 9: $|xy| = |x| \cdot |y|$ for every x and y and $\left|\dfrac{x}{y}\right| = \dfrac{|x|}{|y|}$, $y \neq 0$.

When x is replaced by $-x$, $|-xy| = |xy|$ by theorem 7.

$$|-x| \cdot |y| = |x| \cdot |y| \text{ and } \left|\dfrac{-x}{y}\right| = \dfrac{|-x|}{|y|} = \dfrac{|x|}{|y|}$$

$\therefore$ the same result is obtained. Similarly the same result is found by replacing y by $-y$.

Hence we may assume $x \geqslant 0$ and $y \geqslant 0$.

In that case, the equations take the form

$$xy = xy \text{ and } \frac{x}{y} = \frac{x}{y} \text{ which is certainly true.}$$

Theorem 10: For every x, y,

$$|x+y| \leqslant |x| + |y|.$$

(i) Suppose $x+y \geqslant 0$. Then $|x+y| = x+y$ by definition. But from theorem 8 above, $x \leqslant |x|$ and $y \leqslant |y|$.

$\therefore |x+y| = x+y \leqslant |x| + |y|$ by adding the two inequalities.

(ii) Suppose $x+y < 0$. Then $(-x)+(-y) > 0$.

Then $|(-x)+(-y)| \leqslant |-x| + |-y|$ from (i) above

i.e. $|-x-y| \leqslant |-x| + |-y|$

From theorem 7 above, $|-x| = |x|$ etc.

$\therefore |x+y| \leqslant |x| + |y|$

Illustrative examples.

Example 10: Prove that for every x and y, $|x-y| \leqslant |x| + |y|$.

We have from theorem 10,

$$|x+y| \leqslant |x| + |y|$$

If we replace y by $-y$,

$$|x-y| \leqslant |x| + |-y|$$

But $|-y| = |y|$ $\therefore |x-y| \leqslant |x| + |y|$.

Example 11: Prove that for every x and y,

$$|x-y| \geqslant |x| - |y|.$$

We have $x-y+y = x$

$\therefore |x-y+y| = |x| \leqslant |x-y| + |y|$

from Theorem 10.

$\therefore |x| - |y| \leqslant |x-y|$ or $|x-y| \geqslant |x| - |y|$.

Example 12: Prove that $|x-y| \geqslant \left| |x| - |y| \right|$

From example 11, we have $|x| - |y| \leqslant |x-y|$

Interchanging x and y, $|y| - |x| \leqslant |y-x| = |x-y|$.

Whether $|x| - |y|$ is positive or negative,

$$|x-y| \geqslant \left| |x| - |y| \right|.$$

Exercise

1. Show that for any real number a, $\sqrt{a^2}=|a|$.

2. For each real number a, show that $-|a| \leqslant a \leqslant |a|$.

3. For $0 < x < 1$, show that $|x-1|=1-x$.

4. Prove that $|a \pm b| \leqslant |a| + |b|$. When does the sign of equality hold?

5. Prove that $|ab|=|a| \cdot |b|$ and that if $b \neq 0$, $\left|\dfrac{a}{b}\right| = \dfrac{|a|}{|b|}$.

6. If $d > 0$, then $|c| \leqslant d$, if and only if $-d \leqslant c \leqslant d$.

7. If $d > 0$, then $|x-a| \leqslant d$ if and only if $a-d \leqslant x \leqslant a+d$.

8. Show that $|a-b| \geqslant \Big| |a|-|b| \Big|$.

9. Show that the inequality $|a| + |b| \geqslant |a+b|$ is equivalent to $|ab| \geqslant \sqrt{ab}$. [*Hint*. Use the algebraic definition $|a| = \sqrt{a^2}$ and $|b| = \sqrt{b^2}$.]

10. Show that the inequality of example 8 is also equivalent to $|ab| \geqslant ab$.

CHAPTER 4

Relations, Functions and Mappings

4.1. Relations and graphs of inequalities.

In Mathematics we deal with a set of elements like numbers and points. To construct a mathematical theory, we need not only these elements but *relations* between them. Consider, for instance, the law of trichotomy. If a and $b \in R$, then one and only one of the following statements is true: $a > b$, $a = b$ or $a < b$. Each one of these statements is a relation between them. Such relations concern two elements and are, therefore, called *binary relations*. There are other relations; for instance, a *ternary* relation which concerns three elements or objects. For instance, if there are three points A, B, C on a line such that A lies between B and C, there is a *ternary* relation between A, B and C. The concept of *relation* is an important one. For a general binary relation between a and b, we write bRa and say that b is in the relation R to a. The relation $a > b$ or $b < a$ means that b belongs to the set of all numbers which are less than a.

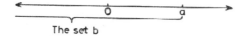

The set b

Graphically the set of numbers (b) with the relation $b < a$ is represented by all the points on the x-axis to the left of A which corresponds to the number a. Here the rule of correspondence bRa between b and a is $b < a$. This implies the existence of a set of numbers b such that $b < a$ and this set is also spoken of as a relation R. Here a relation R is a set to be distinguished from the rule bRa (i.e. $b < a$). If X is the set of all real numbers corresponding to points on the x-axis, R is a subset of the *domain X*.

Similarly in two dimensional space (i.e. in a plane) a point

41

is determined by two coordinates x and y. There may be relation between x and y. All points on the plane are represented by the cross-product $X \cdot Y$, where X is the set of real numbers on the x-axis and Y is the set of real numbers on the y-axis. If with each element of set X, there is associated an element of set Y, then this association constitutes a relation from X to Y.

The rule of association or relation between y and x, is yRx and this rule gives rise to a set of ordered pairs (x, y) which is, of course, a subset of $X \cdot Y$. The set X is called the *domain* of the relation R and set Y is called its *range*. We shall consider some such relations here graphically.

Example 1: Let the relation R be $y \geqslant x$.

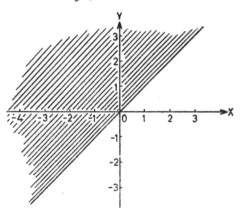

The shaded part to the left of the line $y = x$ including the line represents the inequality $y \geqslant x$. Notice that for a given x, there are an infinite number of y^s satisfying the relation. The graph is half of the plane.

Here the set $R = \{(x, y) \mid y \geqslant x, x \in X, y \in Y\}$.

Example 2: Draw the graph of the relation $|x| + |y| \leqslant 1$.

Here we consider values in each quadrant of the $(x\,y)$ plane separately.

In the first quadrant $x \geqslant 0$, $\quad y \geqslant 0$; $\therefore |x| + |y| = \quad x + y$

In the second quadrant $x \leqslant 0$, $\quad y \geqslant 0$ $\therefore |x| + |y| = -x + y$

In the third quadrant $x \leqslant 0$, $\quad y \leqslant 0$ $\therefore |x| + |y| = -x - y$

and in the fourth quadrant $x \geqslant 0, y \leqslant 0$ $\therefore |x| + |y| = \quad x - y$

The graph of the relation is shown by the shaded part bounded by four sides.

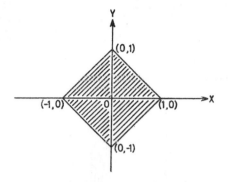

The graph of the inequality is bounded by the straight line $x+y=1$ in the first quadrant, $y-x=1$ in the second quadrant, $-(x+y)=1$ in the third quadrant and $x-y=1$ in the fourth quadrant. For every point inside the square, the inequality $|x|+|y|<1$ is satisfied and so also on the four boundary lines $|x|+|y|=1$. In each quadrant, for a given x there are an infinite number of ys satisfying the relation $|x|+|y| \leqslant 1$. Outside the square, the relation is $|x|+|y|>1$.

Example 3: Draw the graph of the relation $x^2+y^2>9$.

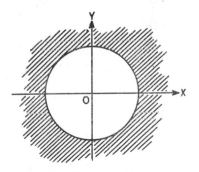

Inside the circle of radius 3 units, every point satisfies the relation $x^2 + y^2 < 9$. Every point on the circle satisfies the relation $x^2 + y^2 = 9$ and every point outside the circle satisfies the relation $x^2 + y^2 > 9$. The shaded part of the plane represents the relation $x^2 + y^2 > 9$. This does not include the points on the boundary.

Example 4: Draw the graph of $y^2 \leqslant 4x$.

Draw the graph of the relation $y^2 = 4x$ in the first instance.

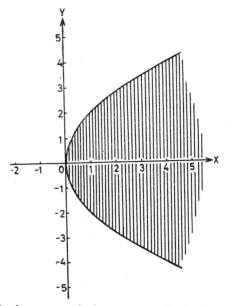

The graph is a parabola symmetrical about the x-axis. Inside the parabola $y^2 < 4x$ and on the parabola $y^2 = 4x$. The shaded portion is the required graph. Outside the parabola $y^2 > 4x$.

4.2. Relations and functions.

In the case of any relation between x and y such as $y \geqslant x$ or $y < x^2 - 2x + 3$, for a given x of X, there are several values of y in the set Y. When there is one and only one y of the set Y for a given x of the set X, the relation yRx is called a functional relation or simply a function. It is usually denoted by $y=f(x)$. Thus $y=x$ and $y=x^2-2x+3$ are instances of functions. In the case of $x^2+y^2=9$, $y=\pm\sqrt{9-x^2}$ and there are two values of y for any given x. y is not, therfore, a function of x. In such cases, we consider two separate functions $y=+\sqrt{1-x^2}$ and $y=-\sqrt{1-x^2}$.

Definition: A function from X to Y is a set of ordered pairs (x, y) such that to each $x \in X$, there corresponds a unique $y \in Y$.

Suppose the set of ordered pairs is $(1, 3)$, $(2, 5)$, $(3, 4)$. Here the set X is $\{1, 2, 3\}$ and the set Y is $\{3, 5, 4\}$. To each x of X, there is a unique y of Y. Hence the set describes a function. The domain and the range are $\{1, 2, 3\}$ and $\{3, 5, 4\}$ respectively.

On the other hand, the set of ordered pairs $(1, 2)$, $(1, 3)$ and $(2, 5)$ describes only a relation, as there are two values of y corresponding to $x=1$. The value of y is not, therefore, unique for $x=1$. The domain is $\{1, 2\}$ and the range is $\{2, 3, 5\}$. If X and Y comprise real numbers, the ordered pairs (x, y) such that $y=f(x)$ represent a particular kind of subset of points in the plane Oxy. In terms of sets, the function f is the set $\{(x, y) \mid x \in X, y \in Y, y=f(x)\}$ of ordered pairs and these ordered pairs trace a kind of curve on the plane of x and y axes. All lines parallel to OY corresponding to the domain of X, intersect the curve in just a single point. This is because, there is a unique y in the range for each specified x of the given domain. The converse is not generally true, for each specified y in the range y of $y=f(x)$, there may be more than one x to correspond. For instance, $y=2x^2$ defined on the domain of real numbers is a function for which $x=1$ and $x=-1$ give the same y viz. 2.

We trace below the curves of function given by
$\{(x, y) \mid 3x + 4y = 8\}$ and $\{(x, y) \mid y = 2x^2\}$.

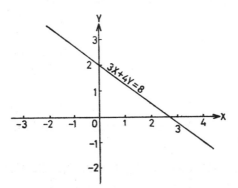

All the points (x, y) on the graph (which is a straight line) satisfy the relation $3x + 4y = 8$. For each x there is a unique y and therefore, y is a function. The domain is R and the range is R.

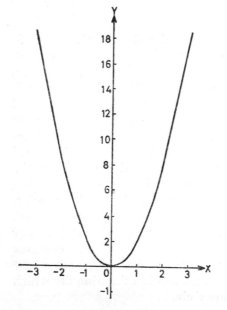

This is the graph of the function $y = 2x^2$. For each x, there is a unique y, although for any given y, there are two values of x. The domain is R, while the range is the set of non-negative real numbers. Here also y is a function. In both the cases, any line $\parallel OY$ cuts the curve in one point only.

4.3. Mapping.

The representation of a function as a curve such as a line or a parabola is the *graphical* aspect of the function. Another important diagrammatic aspect is that of a function as a *mapping*. As we have seen, a function f is the set $\{(x, y) \mid x \in X, y \in Y, y = f(x)\}$. For a given $x \in X$, the corresponding y is unique. If the ordered pair (a, b) belongs to the function i.e. if $f(a) = b$, we say that b is the *image* of a under f so that in general, the range is the image of its domain.

Definition: Let X and Y be two sets of real numbers. The function $y = f(x)$ defined on X and with a subset of Y as a range, gives a mapping of the set X into the set Y such that to each $x \in X$, there is a unique image $f(x) \in Y$.

For instance, let X and Y be the sets of positive integers 1, 2, 3, ...

The mapping $y = 3x - 1$ can be illustrated in the figure below

X		Y
6	$\longrightarrow$	17
5	$\longrightarrow$	14
4	$\longrightarrow$	11
3	$\longrightarrow$	8
2	$\longrightarrow$	5
1	$\longrightarrow$	2

$f(x)$ here is a subset of positive integers. $y = 3x - 1$ is a mapping of X into itself, as the range 2, 5, 8 ...... is a subset of the positive integers.

Since for every x there is a unique y and for every y, there is a unique x, we say that the mapping is one-one. The mapping is generally many-one. That is, for two or more values of x, there is one and the same y. For instance, $y = x^2$ is a mapping of the set X of all real numbers *into* itself, but the mapping is *two-one*. For, both $x = -2$ and $+2$ have a corresponding value of 4 for y. The sets X and Y are generally different. It is a special case when X is mapped into itself.

Exercise

Draw the graphs of the following and state which of them are relations and which are functions:

1. $y = -|x|.$ **2.** $y = \frac{1}{2}(x - |x|).$

3. $y = \frac{1}{2}(|x| - x).$ **4.** $y = \frac{1}{2}(x + |x|).$

5. $y > 2x - 3.$ **6.** $y < 3x + 4.$

7. $y = |x| + |x - 1|.$ **8.** $y = 2|x + 1| + |x| + |x - 1| - 3.$

9. $y = x^2 - x - 6.$ **10.** $y < -4x^2.$

11. Sketch the graph of the relation represented by the set of ordered pairs $\{(x, y) \mid y < |x - 2|\}.$

12. Draw the graph of the relation $\{(x, y) \mid y^2 = x.\}$

13. Draw the graph of the function $\{(x, y) \mid y = 4x^2 - 1\}.$

14. X and Y comprise all positive real numbers $(x > 0, y > 0)$. Draw the graph of the relation $x^2 + y^2 < 1.$

15. Show that the mapping of $y = 2x - 3$ where the domain is R is both *one-one* and *into*.

CHAPTER 5

Complex Numbers

Further extension of the number system is both necessary and possible. In a previous chapter, we have dealt with real numbers which are an extension to the system of rational numbers like $\frac{3}{5}$, $-\frac{2}{3}$ etc. The rational numbers themselves are an extension of the system of integers, positive and negative. The necessity of further extension of the concept of numbers arises from the fact that with them we are not able to solve an equation of the type $x^2+4=0$. This leads us to the algebra of complex numbers. We, however, begin with a more general system of ordered pairs of real numbers.

5.1. Algebra of ordered pairs.

Any two real numbers form a pair of real numbers. If the pair is ordered i.e. we make sure which one is first and which is second, it is called an ordered pair of real numbers. It is usual to write it as (x, y), where x and y are any two real numbers, x comes first and y second. In this way we develop the algebra of all ordered pairs of real numbers. Two ordered pairs (x_1, y_1) and (x_2, y_2) are said to be equal if and only if $x_1=x_2$ and $y_1=y_2$. Let us denote the set of all ordered pairs of real numbers by P so that

$$P = \{(x, y) \mid x, y \in R\}.$$

To carry on the ordinary operations of algebra, we need first of all the two definitions of addition and multiplication of ordered pairs.

Definition: The sum of two ordered pairs (x_1, y_1) and (x_2, y_2) is the ordered pair (x_1+x_2, y_1+y_2).

This is written $(x_1, y_1) + (x_2, y_2) = (x_1 + x_2, \ y_1 + y_2)$.
For example, $(2, \ -1) + (-3, \ 2) = (-1, \ 1)$ and
$$(-2, \ 3) + (2, \ -3) = (0, \ 0).$$
Generally, $(x, y) + (-x, \ -y) = (0, \ 0)$ for all x, y.
Now $(0, 0)$ is an ordered pair such that $(x, y) + (0, \ 0) = (x, y)$.
∴ an additive inverse element exists, vide postulate 7 in chapter 2.

Subtraction of ordered pairs is carried on in the same way as in the case of rational or real numbers.

If $(x_1, y_1) + (x, y) = (x_2, y_2)$,
then $(x, y) = (x_2, y_2) - (x_1, y_1)$.
Here $x + x_1 = x_2$ and $y + y_1 = y_2$ so that
$x = x_2 - x_1$ and $y = y_2 - y_1$.
Thus $(5, 3) - (2, -1) = (3, 4)$.

Definition: The product of the ordered pairs (x_1, y_1) and (x_2, y_2) is the ordered pair $(x_1 x_2 - y_1 y_2, \ x_1 y_2 + x_2 y_1)$.
For example, $(2, 3) \cdot (-1, 5) = (-2 - 15, \ 10 - 3)$ or $(-17, 7)$.

Note that $(x, y) \cdot (1, 0) = (x, y)$ so that the identity element for multiplication exists in the set of ordered pairs (vide postulate 6 in chapter 2).

Division: If $(x_2, y_2) \cdot (x, y) = (x_1, y_1)$ where
$(x_2, y_2) \neq (0, 0)$, then $(x, y) = \dfrac{(x_1, y_1)}{(x_2, y_2)}$.
Since $x_1 = x x_2 - y y_2 \ \dots \ (1)$ and $y_1 = x y_2 + x_2 y \ \dots \ (2)$,
we have $x = \dfrac{x_1 x_2 + y_1 y_2}{x_2{}^2 + y_2{}^2}, \quad y = \dfrac{x_2 y_1 - x_1 y_2}{x_2{}^2 + y_2{}^2}$ by
solving the two equations (1) and (2) for x and y.
$$\therefore \ (x, y) = \frac{(x_1, y_1)}{(x_2, y_2)} = \left(\frac{x_1 x_2 + y_1 y_2}{x_2{}^2 + y_2{}^2}, \ \frac{x_2 y_1 - x_1 y_2}{x_2{}^2 + y_2{}^2} \right)$$

These definitions will meet all our requirements to satisfy the postulates given in chapter 2.

(a) Since $(x_1, y_1) + (x_2, y_2) = (x_1 + x_2, y_1 + y_2)$ and $(x_1, y_1) \cdot (x_2, y_2) = (x_1 x_2 - y_1 y_2, x_1 y_2 + x_2 y_1)$, the postulate of closure is satisfied; for, the resulting ordered pairs $(x_1 + x_2, y_1 + y_2)$ and $(x_1 x_2 - y_1 y_2, x_1 y_2 + x_2 y_1)$ belong to the system of ordered pairs of real numbers.

(b) Commutative and distributive laws are also satisfied; for

$$(x_1, y_1) + (x_2, y_2) = (x_2, y_2) + (x_1, y_1) = (x_1 + x_2, y_1 + y_2)$$
$$= (x_2 + x_1, y_2 + y_1)$$

and $(x_1, y_1) \cdot (x_2, y_2) = (x_2, y_2) \cdot (x_1, y_1)$
$$= (x_1 x_2 - y_1 y_2, x_1 y_2 + x_2 y_1)$$
$$= (x_2 x_1 - y_2 y_1, x_2 y_1 + x_1 y_2)$$

Since $x_1 + x_2$, $x_1 x_2$, etc. are commutative, these additions and products are also commutative. We can verify the distributive law also.

(c) The addition and multiplication are also associative, as we can easily show that

$$[(x_1, y_1) + (x_2, y_2)] + (x_3, y_3) = (x_1, y_1) + [(x_2, y_2) + (x_3, y_3)]$$

and $[(x_1, y_1) \cdot (x_2, y_2)] \cdot (x_3, y_3) = (x_1, y_1) \cdot [(x_2, y_2) \cdot (x_3, y_3).].$

(d) We have already seen that there are identity elements for addition and multiplication viz. $(0, 0)$ and $(1, 0)$. Since $(x, y) + (-x, -y) = (0, 0)$, there is an additive inverse or negative element $(-x, -y)$ for every (x, y).

(e) There is a multiplicative inverse also for every (x, y).

$$(x, y) \cdot \left(\frac{x}{x^2 + y^2}, \frac{-y}{x^2 + y^2} \right) = (1, 0).$$

The multiplicative inverse of (x, y) is $\left(\dfrac{x}{x^2 + y^2}, \dfrac{-y}{x^2 + y^2} \right)$.

(f) The set of ordered pairs is unique.

If $(x_1, y_1) = (x_2, y_2)$ and $(x_3, y_3) = (x_4, y_4)$, then
$(x_1, y_1) + (x_3, y_3) = (x_2, y_2) + (x_4, y_4)$
$= (x_1 + x_3, y_1 + y_3) = (x_2 + x_4, y_2 + y_4)$ as
the real numbers $x_1 + x_3 = x_2 + x_4$ and $y_1 + y_3 = y_2 + y_4$.

Similarly we can show that $(x_1, y_1) \cdot (x_3, y_3) = (x_2, y_2) \ (x_4, y_4)$ as $x_1 x_3 - y_1 y_3 = x_2 x_4 - y_2 y_4$ etc.

Thus the set P is a field (vide last para of 2-3.)

Exercise 5·1

Find the ordered pair for,

1. $(2, 3) + (-3, -1)$. **2.** $(-3, 4) + (-2, 4)$.

3. $(3, 5) \cdot (1, -2)$. **4.** $(2, -7) \cdot (-1, 2)$.

5. $(3, 2) - (1, 3)$. **6.** $(7, 5) - (-1, -3)$.

7. $(1, 2) - (3, -2)$. **8.** $(a, b) \cdot (c, d) - (-a, -b) \cdot (-c, -d)$

9. $\dfrac{(2, 5)}{(1, 2)}$. **10.** $\dfrac{(3, 2)}{(2, 3)}$. **11.** $\dfrac{(13, 7)}{(5, -1)}$.

12. Show that $(3, 5) \cdot (0, 0) = (0, 0)$.

13. Prove that $(0, 1) \cdot (0, 1)$ or $(0, 1)^2 = (-1, 0)$.

14. Prove that $(a, b) = (b, a)$ if and only if $a = b$.

15. Find the value of $\dfrac{(1, 0)}{(x, y)}$. What is the reciprocal of $(2, -1)$?

16. Show that $(a, b) \ [(1, 2) + (2, 3)] = (a, b) \cdot (1, 2) + (a, b) \cdot (2, 3)$.

5.2. Complex numbers.

The algebra of the complex numbers is one of the common interpretations of the algebra of ordered pairs. In fact, we define a complex number as an ordered pair, written not as (x, y) but as $x + iy$, where x and y are real numbers. With a new element i, where $i^2 = -1$, $x + iy$ may be thought of as the same thing as an ordered pair of real numbers. If $y = 0$, the complex number $x + iy$ becomes real. If y is not zero, the complex number is said to be *imaginary*. Thus the real numbers are included in the set of complex numbers or $R \subset C$, where C is the set of complex numbers.

It is usual to denote a complex number by z which stands for $x + iy$. Here x is called the real part and y the imaginary part of z.

$$z_1 + z_2 = (x_1 + iy_1) + (x_2 + iy_2) = (x_1 + x_2) + i(y_1 + y_2)$$
$$z_1 \cdot z_2 = (x_1 + iy_1) \cdot (x_2 + iy_2) = x_1 x_2 + ix_1 y_2 + ix_2 y_1 - y_1 y_2.$$
$$= (x_1 x_2 - y_1 y_2) + i(x_1 y_2 + x_2 y_1)$$

As a particular case, the product of a real number a and a complex number $x + iy = ax + iay$.

We see that the sum and product of two complex numbers satisfy the same laws as the ordered pairs.

Similarly we can perform the operations of subtraction and division.

$$z_1 - z_2 = (x_1 + iy_1) - (x_2 + iy_2) = (x_1 - x_2) + i(y_1 - y_2)$$
$$\text{and } \frac{z_1}{z_2} = \frac{x_1 + iy_1}{x_2 + iy_2} = \frac{(x_1 + iy_1)(x_2 - iy_2)}{(x_2 + iy_2)(x_2 - iy_2)}$$
$$= \frac{x_1 x_2 - ix_1 y_2 + ix_2 y_1 + y_1 y_2}{x_2{}^2 + y_2{}^2} \quad \text{since } i^2 = -1$$
$$= \frac{(x_1 x_2 + y_1 y_2) + i(x_2 y_1 - x_1 y_2)}{x_2{}^2 + y_2{}^2}$$

Compare these results with those of the previous section. They are exactly the same as those of ordered pairs. The complex numbers satisfy all the postulates—Closure, Associative, Commutative and Distributive Laws, Identity elements, Additive and Multiplicative inverses and Uniqueness —as in the case of rational and real numbers, in exactly the same way as ordered pairs. The set of complex numbers is, therefore, a *field*. Two complex numbers z_1 and z_2 which differ only in the sign of their imaginary parts are called *conjugate* of each other. That is, $x + iy$ and $x - iy$ are *conjugate* complex numbers. If $z = x + iy$, z, the conjugate is $x - iy$.

Although we use the word 'imaginary' for a complex number or the word 'imaginary part' of a complex number, the complex numbers should not be regarded as a sort of vague idea. They are as real in Mathematics and as significant in their application to physics and engineering, as any other numbers. These numbers were originally introduced to solve quadratic equations. For instance, $x^2-2x+3=0$ has two roots,

$$x = \frac{2\pm\sqrt{4-12}}{2} = \frac{2\pm\sqrt{-8}}{2} = \frac{2\pm2\sqrt{-2}}{2}$$
$$= 1\pm\sqrt{2}i, \text{ as } \sqrt{-2}=\sqrt{(-1)2} = \sqrt{2}\sqrt{-1}=\sqrt{2}i.$$

Example 1 : If any expression involving complex numbers is zero, the real part and the imaginary part are separately zero.

Let $x+iy=0$ $\therefore$ $x=-iy$ where x and y are real numbers.

Squaring both sides $x \cdot x=(-iy) \cdot (-iy)$ or
$x^2=(+i)^2y^2=-y^2$

Since y^2 is positive, the square of a real number x is negative.   This is not possible unless each of x and y is zero.

Thus if an expression reduces to $A+iB$ and is equal to zero, $A=0$ and $B=0$.

Example 2 : Simplify: $\dfrac{1}{1+i}$.

$$\frac{1}{1+i}=\frac{1(1-i)}{(1+i)(1-i)}=\frac{1-1i}{1-i^2}=\tfrac{1}{2}-\tfrac{1}{2}i.$$

Exercise 5·2

Express as a single complex number:

1. $2+3i+3-5i$.

2. $3+4i+6i+5$.

3. $(5+4i)-(3+2i)$.

4. $1+i+3i^2+5i$.

5. $3(10-5i)$.

6. $(1+i)(2+i)$.

7. $(3+4i)(3-4i)$.

8. $(2+\sqrt{2}i)(3-i)$.

9. $(2+i\sqrt{3})(3-\sqrt{-12})$.

10. If n is any positive integer, show that $i^{4n}=1$ and $i^{4n+1}=i$.

11. $(5+\sqrt{-5})^2$.

12. $(3+i\sqrt{2})(3-2\sqrt{-8})$.

13. $(5-\sqrt{-18})(1-\sqrt{-2})$.

14. $(1-i\sqrt{2})^2$.

15. $(\sqrt{3}-i)^3$.

16. $(-\sqrt{3}-i)^3$.

17. $\dfrac{1}{3+2i}$.

18. $\dfrac{1}{2i}$.

19. $\dfrac{1}{2i-5}$.

20. $\dfrac{1}{3-i\sqrt{2}}$.

21. $\dfrac{1}{(4-\sqrt{-12})^2}$.

22. $\dfrac{3+2i}{1-i}$.

23. $\dfrac{1+4i}{3-2i}$.

24. $\dfrac{3+5i}{2i}$.

25. $\dfrac{1}{i}$.

26. $\dfrac{1-i}{1+i}$.

27. $\dfrac{3+2i}{2-3i}$.

28. $\dfrac{5-7i}{3-2i}$.

29. $\left(\dfrac{1-i}{1+i}\right)^2$.

30. $\left(\dfrac{3-\sqrt{5}i}{3+\sqrt{5}i}\right)^2$.

31. Prove that $x+iy=a+ib$ if and only if $x=a$ and $y=b$ where x, y, a, b are real numbers.

Using this result, solve the following equations for the real numbers x and y:

32. $(2+i)^2+2(x-iy)=3(x+iy)$.

33. $(3+4i)^2-2(x-iy)=(2+3i)^2+x+iy$.

34. $\left(\dfrac{1+i}{1-i}\right)^2+\dfrac{1}{x+iy}=1+i$.

35. $(2-3i)(x+iy)=2(x-iy)+2i+1$.

5.3. The modulus of a complex number.

The set of complex numbers is not an ordered field. That is to say, we cannot state when $z_1 > z_2$ or $z_1 < z_2$. This is due to the fact that a complex number consists of two parts — one real and another imaginary. However, we can compare two complex numbers by their absolute values.

Definition: If $z = x + iy$ where x and y are two real numbers, the absolute value of z is $\sqrt{x^2 + y^2}$.

This value is supposed to be always positive and it is a real number. The absolute value of z is written $|z|$.

$|z| = |x + iy| = \sqrt{(x^2 + y^2)}$. The positive square root of $x^2 + y^2$ is called the *modulus* of $x + iy$.

When the imaginary part of z is zero,

$|z| = \sqrt{x^2} = |x|$. As we have seen in the preceding chapter, $|x| = x$ if $x \geq 0$ and $|x| = -x$ if $x < 0$.

One interesting inequality in the theory of complex numbers is

$|z_1| + |z_2| \geq |z_1 + z_2|$ or $|z_1 + z_2| \leq |z_1| + |z_2|$.

Let $z_1 = x_1 + iy_1$, and $z_2 = x_2 + iy_2$.

$z_1 + z_2 = (x_1 + x_2) + i(y_1 + y_2)$

$\therefore$ modulus of $z_1 + z_2 = |(x_1 + x_2) + i(y_1 + y_2)|$

$$= \sqrt{(x_1 + x_2)^2 + (y_1 + y_2)^2}$$
$$= \sqrt{x_1^2 + x_2^2 + y_1^2 + y_2^2 + 2x_1 x_2 + 2y_1 y_2}$$

and modulus of $z_1 = \sqrt{x_1^2 + y_1^2}$, mod. $z_2 = \sqrt{x_2^2 + y_2^2}$.

Let $|z_1| + |z_2| = \sqrt{x_1^2 + y_1^2} + \sqrt{x_2^2 + y_2^2} = p$

and $|z_1 + z_2| = q$ where p and q are positive real numbers.

Required to prove that $p > q$ or $p^2 > q^2$.

Now $p^2 = x_1^2 + y_1^2 + x_2^2 + y_2^2 + 2\sqrt{(x_1^2 + y_1^2)(x_2^2 + y_2^2)}$ ....(1)

and $q^2 = x_1^2 + y_1^2 + x_2^2 + y_2^2 + 2(x_1 x_2 + y_1 y_2)$ ....(2)

Also $(x_1 x_2 + y_1 y_2)^2 = x_1^2 x_2^2 + y_1^2 y_2^2 + 2x_1 x_2 y_1 y_2$............(3)

$(x_1^2 + y_1^2)(x_2^2 + y_2^2) = x_1^2 x_2^2 + x_1^2 y_2^2 + x_2^2 y_1^2 + y_1^2 y_2^2$........(4)

But $x_1^2 y_2^2 + x_2^2 y_1^2 - 2x_1 x_2 y_1 y_2 = (x_1 y_2 - x_2 y_1)^2 > 0$

$\therefore x_1^2 y_2^2 + x_2^2 y_1^2 > 2x_1 x_2 y_1 y_2$ unless $x_1 y_2 = x_2 y_1$ in which case the inequality becomes equality. $\therefore$ expression, (4) $\geq$ exp. (3).

$\therefore \sqrt{(x_1^2 + y_1^2)(x_2^2 + y_2^2)} \geq x_1 x_2 + y_1 y_2$

$\therefore q^2 \leq p^2$ or $q \leq p$.

$\therefore |z_1 + z_2| \leq |z_1| + |z_2|$.

5.4. Graphical representation of complex numbers.

Since a complex number $x+iy$ is regarded as an ordered

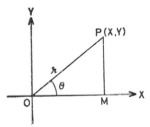

pair of real numbers (x, y), we can represent a complex number as a point in the plane of x and y axes. Take any two perpendicular lines on a plane, as x and y axes. Then $x+iy$ represents the point whose abscissa is x and ordinate is y. The real part of a complex number $x+iy$ lies on the

x-axis and the imaginary part on the y-axis. The modulus of
$$x+iy=\sqrt{x^2+y^2}=\sqrt{OM^2+PM^2}=r \text{ or } OP.$$

If θ is the angle made by OP with the x-axis,
$$x=r\cos\theta \text{ and } y=r\sin\theta.$$
$$\therefore z=r(\cos\theta+i\sin\theta) \text{ where } r^2=x^2+y^2.$$

Here r is the absolute value or modulus of the complex number $z=x+iy$. The angle θ is called the *amplitude* or *argument* of $x+iy$.

Thus every complex number $x+iy$ can be represented by a point in the plane. Conversely every point in the plane is associated with a complex number. This plane is called the complex plane. The graphical representation is known as the *Argand diagram* after a French Mathematician Argand (1768–1822).

By joining the point P to the origin, we have OP whose length is r and which makes an angle θ with the x-axis. Any segment of a line from two points like O and P having both length and direction is called a *vector*. Here $\overrightarrow{OP}$ is a vector, as it has length r and direction (making an angle θ with the

x-axis). Thus we can also represent a complex number by a vector or a directed line-segment. Vectors are useful for the representation of any elements with magnitude and direction such as velocity, acceleration, force etc. Any two parallel and equal line-segments represent the same vector. Any vector AB is represented by $\overrightarrow{AB}$.

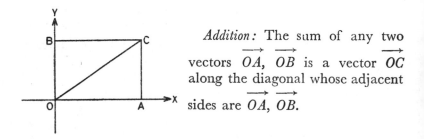

Addition: The sum of any two vectors $\overrightarrow{OA}$, $\overrightarrow{OB}$ is a vector $\overrightarrow{OC}$ along the diagonal whose adjacent sides are $\overrightarrow{OA}$, $\overrightarrow{OB}$.

This can be easily verified if OA lies on the x-axis and OB on the y-axis.

The coordinates of A are (x, o) and the coordinates of B are (o, y) so that $\overrightarrow{OA} + \overrightarrow{OB} = (x+iy)$
$$= \overrightarrow{OC}$$

where OC is the diagonal of the rectangle $OACB$. OA represents the complex number $x+i \cdot o$ and OB represents the complex number $o+iy$.

Now let us consider the general case where $\overrightarrow{OA}=x_1+iy_1$ and $\overrightarrow{OB}=x_2+iy_2$.

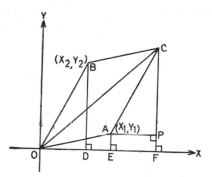

Complete the parallelogram $OACB$ and draw BD, AE, CF $\perp OX$ and $AP \perp CF$.

Vector OB=vector AC, as $OB=AC$ in length and $OB \parallel AC$. They make the same angle with x-axis.

$\therefore \angle BOD = \angle CAP, \angle BDO = \angle CPA$ =a right angle. Also, $AC=OB$.

$\therefore \triangle$s OBD, CAP are congruent.

$\therefore CP=BD=y_2$ and $AE=PF=y_1$

Also $AP=OD=EF=x_2$.

$\therefore OF=OE+EF=x_1+x_2$

$\therefore$ the coordinates of C are (x_1+x_2, y_1+y_2).

$\therefore$ vector OC represents the complex number

$$(x_1+x_2)+i(y_1+y_2).$$

$\therefore \overrightarrow{OA}+\overrightarrow{OB}=(x_1+x_2)+i(y_1+y_2)=\overrightarrow{OC}.$

We can now geometrically see that $|z_1+z_2| \leqslant |z_1|+|z_2|$.

In the $\triangle OAC$, $\overrightarrow{OA}=x_1+iy_1$ or z_1,

$\overrightarrow{OB}=\overrightarrow{AC}=x_2+iy_2$ or z_2 and $\overrightarrow{OC}=z_1 + z_2=\overrightarrow{OA}+\overrightarrow{OB}$.

Now $|z_1| = OA$ (in length)

$|z_2| = OB$,,

$|z_1+z_2) = OC$,,

But in the $\triangle OAC$, $OA+AC > OC$.   If OA and OB are in the same line, $OC=OA+OB$ in length. $\therefore$ $OA+AC \geqslant OC$. Hence the result.

Example 3: Represent the complex numbers or vectors $2+3i$, $2-3i$, $-2+3i$, $-2-3i$ and find the modulus in each case.

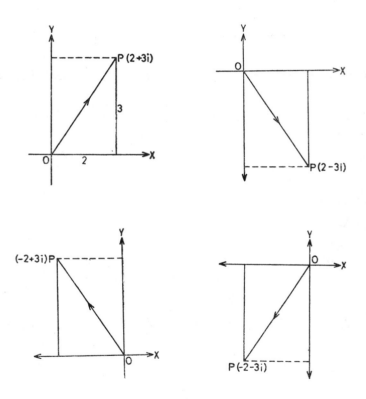

The coordinates of P in these 4 cases are $(2, 3)$, $(2, -3)$, $(-2, 3)$ and $(-2, -3)$ and the modulus in each case is $OP=\sqrt{4+9}=\sqrt{13}$.

Example 4: Express the complex number $-3+4i$ in the form $r(\cos\theta+i\sin\theta)$.

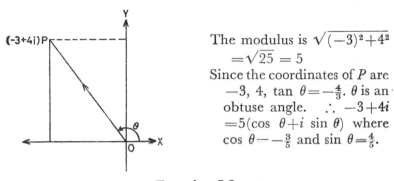

The modulus is $\sqrt{(-3)^2+4^2}$
$=\sqrt{25}=5$

Since the coordinates of P are -3, 4, $\tan\theta=-\frac{4}{3}$. θ is an obtuse angle. $\therefore$ $-3+4i$ $=5(\cos\theta+i\sin\theta)$ where $\cos\theta=-\frac{3}{5}$ and $\sin\theta=\frac{4}{5}$.

Exercise 5·3

Find the modulus of the complex numbers.

1. $1+i$.   **2.** $1-i$.   **3.** $2i$.   **4.** $5-12i$.

5. $2+3i+(3+i)$.   **6.** $5+6i-(1+2i)$.

7. $\dfrac{1+2i}{1-2i}$.   **8.** $\dfrac{2+3i}{3-4i}$.   **9.** $\dfrac{3+4i}{2i}$.

10. Show that the complex number $z=0$ if and only if the modulus of z is 0.

11. Show that the modulus of a complex number is the same as that of its conjugate.

12. Show that $z\cdot\bar{z}=|z|^2$ where $\bar{z}$ is the conjugate of z.

13. For any complex number $z=x+iy$, show that $x\leqslant|z|$ and $y\leqslant|z|$.

14. Prove that $|z_1 z_2|=|z_1|\cdot|z_2|$ where z_1 and z_2 are any two complex numbers. [Assume $z_1=x_1+iy_1$ and $z_2=x_2+iy_2$.]

15. Prove that $|15+9i|<|3+4i|+|12+5i|$.

16. Represent graphically z_1-z_2.
[To subtract x_2+iy_2 from x_1+iy_1, add $-x_2-iy_2$ to x_1+iy_1.]

17. Show that the vectors $3+2i$ and $3-2i$ make equal angles with the x-axis on opposite sides.

18. Find graphically:
   (a) $(1+3i)+(2+2i)$
   (b) $(1+3i)-(2+2i)$.

19. Construct the sum and difference graphically:
   (a) $(3+2i)+(2-3i)$
   (b) $(3+2i)-(2-3i)$.

20. Express $1+4i$, $1-4i$, $-\frac{1}{2}+\frac{\sqrt{3}i}{2}$, $-\frac{1}{2}-\frac{\sqrt{3}i}{2}$ in   the   form $r\,(\cos\,\theta+i\,\sin\,\theta)$.

CHAPTER 6

The Euclid's Algorithm

6.1. You are familiar with the process of finding the H.C.F. of any two integers in Arithmetic. Suppose you want the H.C.F. of 987 and 1449. You may not be able to guess the factors of each easily. In that case, you follow the following process:

$$
\begin{array}{cccc}
\underline{1} & \underline{2} & \underline{7} & \underline{3} \\
987)\ \overline{1449} & 462)\ \overline{987} & 63)\ \overline{462} & 21)\ \overline{63} \\
987 & 924 & 441 & 63 \\
\overline{462} & \overline{63} & \overline{21} & \overline{0}
\end{array}
$$

The H.C.F. of the two integers is 21. We first divide the greater integer by the other one. We have 462 as the remainder. We now divide the given smaller integer 987 (or the divisor) by the remainder in the first division. We have again a remainder of 63. We now divide 462 by 63 and get 21 as the remainder. Finally we divide the previous divisor by the remainder viz. 21, and see that there is no remainder. Then we conclude that 21, the last non-zero remainder is the H.C.F. of the two given integers. This process of repeated division is known as Euclid's Algorithm. Algorithm means a rule for computation and is derived from the surname of an Arab Mathematician. This rule is followed mechanically in Arithmetic, but it can be proved, as shown in the next section.

6.2. If a and b are positive integers such that $b \leqslant a$, and $a \div b = q$ with a remainder r, then $a = bq + r$, where $0 \leqslant r < b$.

If $r = 0$, b is a factor of a or a is a multiple of b. In this division, q and r are unique.

Theorem 1: Any common factor c of a and b is a factor of r and any common factor d of b and r is a factor of a.

Let $a=cx$ and $b=cy$ so that when b is divided by a, we have, $a=cx=bq+r=cyq+r$.

$\therefore r=cx-cyq=c(x-yq)$

Here r, c and $x-yq$ are non-negative integers.

$\therefore c$ is a factor of r.

In the second case, let $b=du$ and $r=dv$.

Since $a=bq+r=duq+dv=d(uq+v)$,

d is a factor of a.

From this theorem it follows that the H.C.F. of a and b is the H.C.F. of b and r.

Now the H.C.F. of a and b, $(a>b)$ can be found by the Euclidean Algorithm. Divide a by b.

The first division gives $a \quad = bq_1+r_1.$

If $r_1 \neq 0$, the second   ,,   ,, $b \quad = r_1q_2+r_2.$

If $r_2 \neq 0$, the third   ,,   ,, $r_1 \quad = r_2q_3+r_3.$

If $r_3 \neq 0$, the fourth   ,,   ,, $r_2 \quad = r_3q_4+r_4.$

     and.................................

If $r_{n-2} \neq 0$, the $n-1$th   ,,   ,, $r_{n-3} = r_{n-2}q_{n-1}+r_{n-1}.$

If $r_{n-1} \neq 0$, the nth   ,,   ,, $r_{n-2} = r_{n-1}q_n +r_n.$

This process continues until a remainder is found equal to zero. This must happen sooner or later since $r_1>r_2>r_3> \cdots$ Let r_n be the last non-zero remainder. This is the H.C.F. of a and b. By theorem 1, the H.C.F. of a and b is also the H.C.F. of b and r_1, the H.C.F. of b and r_1 is also the H.C.F. of r_1 and r_2, and so on until we conclude that the H.C.F. of a and b is the H.C.F. of r_{n-2} and r_{n-1} and of r_{n-1} and r_n.

But $r_{n-1} = r_nq_{n+1}$ without any remainder.

$\therefore r_n$ is factor of r_{n-1} and the H.C.F. of r_{n-1} and r_n is r_n itself.

$\therefore r_n$ is the H.C.F. of a and b.

Theorem 2: If h is the H.C.F. of a and b, there exist positive or negative integers k and l such that $h=ka+lb$.

Now we have from the discussion above,

$$r_n = r_{n-2} - r_{n-1}q_n = r_{n-2} - q_n\,(r_{n-3} - r_{n-2}q_{n-1})$$
$$= -r_{n-3}q_n + (1 + q_n q_{n-1})\,r_{n-2}$$

. . . .

$$= \text{(some integer)}\,a + \text{(some integer)}\,b, \text{ going backwards}$$
through all the stages.

We may call these integers k and l. Hence the result.

Example 1: The H.C.F. of 15 and 25 is 5. Find k and l where $5 = 15k + 25l$.

In the process of finding the H.C.F. by Euclid's Algorithm

$$
\begin{array}{lll}
\ \ 1 & \ \ 1 & \ \ 2 \\
15)\ \overline{25} & 10)\ \overline{15} & 5)\ \overline{10} \\
\ 15 & \ 10 & \ 10 \\
\ \overline{10} & \ \overline{5} & \ \overline{0}
\end{array}
\qquad \therefore \text{ the H.C.F. is 5.}
$$

$r_1 = 10 = 25 - 1 \cdot 15$ and $r_2 = 5 = 15 - 10 \cdot 1$

$\therefore\ r_2 = 5 = 15 - (25 - 15) = 2 \cdot 15\quad 25$

$\therefore\ k = 2$ and $1 = -1$

Example 2: Express the H.C.F. of 66 and 180 as $66k + 180l$.

$$
\begin{array}{l}
\ \ 2 \\
66)\ \overline{180} \\
\ 132 \\
\ \overline{48}
\end{array}
\qquad \therefore\ r_1 = 48 = 180 - 2 \times 66
$$

$$
\begin{array}{l}
\ \ 1 \\
48)\ \overline{66} \\
\ 48 \\
\ \overline{18}
\end{array}
\qquad \therefore\ r_2 = 18 = 66 - 48 \times 1
$$

$$
\begin{array}{l}
\ \ 2 \\
18)\ \overline{48} \\
\ 36 \\
12\ \overline{}
\end{array}
\qquad \therefore\ r_3 = 12 = 48 - 2 \times 18
$$

$$
\begin{array}{l}
\ \ 1 \\
12)\ \overline{18} \\
\ 12 \\
\ \overline{6}
\end{array}
\qquad r_4 = 6 = 18 - 1 \times 12
$$

Now 12 is exactly divisible by 6.

$$\therefore \text{ H.C.F. is } 6.$$

Working backwards,

$$r_4 = 6 = 18 - 12 = 18 - r_3 = 18 - (48 - 2 \times 18)$$
$$= 3 \cdot 18 - 48 = 3r_2 - 48$$
$$= 3(66 - 48) - 48 = 3 \cdot 66 - 4 \cdot 48$$
$$= 3 \times 66 - 4r_1 = 3 \times 66 - 4(180 - 2 \times 66)$$
$$= 11 \times 66 - 4 \times 180$$

$$\therefore k = 11 \text{ and } 1 = -4$$

Check: $6 = 66 \times 11 - 4 \times 180 = 726 - 720.$

Example 3: Find the H.C.F. of 413 and 588 and express it in the form $413k + 588l$.

(i)
$$413 \overline{)\ 588} \qquad \therefore r_1 = 175 = 588 - 413$$
$$413$$
$$\overline{175}$$
with quotient 1.

(ii)
$$175 \overline{)\ 413} \qquad \therefore r_2 = 63 = 413 - 2 \times 175$$
$$350$$
$$\overline{63}$$
with quotient 2.

(iii)
$$63 \overline{)\ 175} \qquad \therefore r_3 = 49 = 175 - 2 \times 63$$
$$126$$
$$\overline{49}$$
with quotient 2.

(iv)
$$49 \overline{)\ 63} \qquad r_4 = 14 = 63 - 49$$
$$49$$
$$\overline{14}$$
with quotient 1.

(v)
$$14 \overline{)\ 49} \qquad r_5 = 7 = 49 - 14 \times 3$$
$$42$$
$$\overline{7}$$
with quotient 3.

7 divides 14 exactly. $\therefore$ 7 is the H.C.F.

$$
\begin{aligned}
\text{Now } 7 &= 49 - 14 \cdot 3 = 49 - 3(63 - 49) \\
&= 4 \cdot 49 - 3 \times 63. \quad \text{Now substitute } r_3 \\
&= 4(175 - 2 \times 63) - 3 \times 63 \\
&= 4 \times 175 - 11 \times 63. \quad \text{Substitute now } r_2 \\
&= 4 \times 175 - 11(413 - 2 \times 175) \\
&= 26 \times 175 - 11 \times 413. \quad \text{Substitute now } r_1 \\
&= 26(588 - 413) - 11 \times 413 \\
&= 26 \times 588 - 37 \times 413 \\
&= 413k + 588l
\end{aligned}
$$

$\therefore k = -37$ and $l = 26$

Check: $588 \times 26 - 413 \times 37 = 15288 - 15281 = 7$.

Hence it is always possible to find k and l such that the H.C.F. of a and $b = ak + bl$.

6.3. *Prime Numbers:* The two positive numbers a and b are said to be *relatively prime* if they have no common factors.

Their H.C.F. is 1. If a and b are relatively prime, then integers k and l exist such that $ka + lb = 1$.

A positive number p is prime if it has no factors other than 1 and p itself. A prime p is also relatively prime to all integers except 1 and multiples of p.

Theorem 3: If p is prime and divides ab, where a and b are positive integers, then either p divides a or p divides b or both.

Proof: If p divides a, there is nothing more to prove. If p does not divide a, then p and a are relatively prime so that $ka + lp = 1$ from the result proved above.

$\therefore kab + lpb = b$, by multiplying b throughout.

But p divides ab (given) and

lpb contains p as a factor.

$\therefore p$ is a factor of b

$\therefore p$ divides b. Hence the result.

Now we are in a position to prove the *Fundamental Theorem of Arithmetic.*

Theorem 4: Every positive integer can be factorised into primes and the factorisation is *unique.*

It is required to prove that for any integer $n, n = p_1 p_2 p_3 \ldots p_i$ for some i.

If n is prime, it is itself the only prime factor. Here $i = 1$ and $p_1 = n$.

If n is not prime, it has factors other than 1 and itself, so that we may write $n = n_1 n_2$ where n_1 and n_2 are both less than n. Now if n_1 and n_2 are not prime, we can find the factors of n_1 and n_2 and proceed to find the further factors of n_1 and n_2. This process stops only when all the factors are primes. This must happen sooner or later as the integers go on getting smaller and smaller.

Now we have to show that these prime factors are unique. If possible, let $n = p_1 p_2 \ldots p_i = q_1 q_2 \ldots q_j$

where p's and q's are unique.

Then p_1 divides n.

$\therefore$ p_1 divides $q_1 q_2 \ldots q_j$.

By theorem 3, p_1 divides at least one of the q's.

Assume that p_1 divides q_1. But p_1 and q_1 are primes and since we have excluded 1 in this result $p_1 = q_1$. Dividing right side by q_1 and the left side by p_1 we have

$$p_2 p_3 \ldots p_i = q_2 q_3 \ldots q_j$$

Treating this result also in the same way we find each p is identical with one of the q's. In the end each p is identified with some q until all are taken.

$\therefore$ $i = j$ and p's and q's are the same set of primes.

This result is known as the Fundamental Theorem of Arithmetic and is used automatically in elementary Arithmetic.

Exercise

By means of the Euclid's Algorithm, find the H.C.F. of the following pairs of numbers:

1. 27, 45.   **2.** 36, 60.   **3.** 60, 75.

4. 37, 75.   **5.** 68, 102.   **6.** 91, 260.

7. 105, 189.   **8.** 348, 203.   **9.** 140, 1155.

10. 156, 306.

11. Show that the H.C.F. of 35 and 25 can be expressed in the form $35k + 25l$. Find k and l.

12. Find the H.C.F. of 465 and 315 and check by the process of repeated division (Euclid's Algorithm). If the H.C.F. $= 465k + 315\,l$, find k and l.

13. Find by Euclid's Algorithm the H.C.F. of 403 and 533 and express it in the form $403k + 533l$.

14. Express 1092 and 330 as products of primes and show that their H.C.F. is 6. Find k and l if $6 = 1092k + 330l$, by Euclid's Algorithm.

15. Find the H.C.F. of 1881 and 1155 and express it in the form $1881k + 1155l$.

16. Prove that if a, b, c are positive integers, a and b being relatively prime, and if a and b are both factors of c, then ab is a factor of c.

CHAPTER 7

Polynomials

7.1. Preliminary.

The word ' polynomial ' is often used both as an adjective and as a noun. Thus we say that a quadratic $3x^2-4x-5$ or a cubic x^3-3x^2+5x+1 are examples of *polynomials* or *polynomial expressions*. When polynomials are equated to zero, we have polynomial equations such as $3x^2-4x-5=0$. Here the problem is to solve the equation and find out the solution set.

In a *polynomial function* such as $y=x^3-3x^2+5x+1$ we have x as a variable with a domain to be specified. The domain may be the set of real numbers or the set of complex numbers. If x is a real number, the function fixes a real number y to correspond to the real number x. If x is a complex number, the corresponding y will be a complex number. If x is an integer or a rational number, so will be y.

We often deal with polynomials in the parametric form, for example, ax^2+bx+c as the general quadratic or ax^3+bx^2+cx+d as the general cubic. Here a, b, c, ... may stand for integers, rational numbers, real numbers or complex numbers, just as x may belong to any system of numbers. For convenience, let us assume that the parameters a, b, c, ... stand for rational numbers. Let us take the simplest polynomial $a+bx$. There will be different polynomials with different values of a and b. Similarly there will be different polynomials with different values of a, b and c in the general quadratic $a+bx+cx^2$. The coefficients of x are all-important in any discussion of polynomials. In fact, we can *define* a polynomial as an ordered set of rational coefficients.

The polynomial of the first degree may be defined as the ordered set of rational coefficients (a, b). The polynomial of the second degree may be taken as the set of rational coefficients (a, b, c), of the third degree as the set of rational coefficients (a, b, c, d) and so on. The order of coefficients matters; it must not be disturbed. Rules for sums and products may be laid down for coefficients as in the case of Algebra of ordered pairs.

Here the rules for the general quadratic are:

(i) $(a_1, b_1, c_1) + (a_2, b_2, c_2) = (a_1 + a_2, b_1 + b_2 \cdot c_1 + c_2)$ for the addition of two quadratics.

For example $(2 + 3x + 5x^2) + (1 + 5x - 2x)^2$
$= (3 + 8x + 3x^2)$

(ii) The rule for multiplication is somewhat difficult.
$(a_1, b_1, c_1) \times (a_2, b_2, c_2)$
$= (a_1 a_2, a_1 b_2 + a_2 b_1, a_1 c_2 + b_1 b_2 + c_1 a_2, b_1 c_2 + b_2 c_1, c_1 c_2)$
This tallies with the actual product of
$(a_1 + b_1 x + c_1 x^2)$ and $(a_2 + b_2 x + c_2 x^2)$. The product is
$a_1 a_2 + (a_1 b_2 + a_2 b_1)x + (a_1 c_2 + b_1 b_2 + c_1 a_2)x^2 + (b_1 c_2 + b_2 c_1)x^3 + c_1 c_2 x^4$.

The rules for addition and multiplication seem to correspond to the ordinary operations of algebra. It will be found that the set of all polynomials obeys the operational rules of sums, differences and multiplications, but there are no reciprocals as there is no division. Polynomials, therefore, form an *integral domain*, with the same properties as the set of integers. Under this scheme, a polynomial is not itself a rational number, or indeed a number at all. In writing $f(x) = a + bx + cx^2 + \ldots\ldots$ we simply specify a set of coefficients $(a, b, c, \ldots\ldots)$ and leave x undefined. x may be a real number or a complex number. This is to be distinguished from $f(a) = a + ba + ca^2 + \ldots.$ where a is a rational number. Here $f(a)$ is also a rational number. If a is a real or complex number, $f(a)$ is also a real or complex number.

7.2. Polynomial functions and equations.

The general polynomial of degree n is:

$f(x) = a_0 x^n + a_1 x^{n-1} + a_2 x^{n-2} + \ldots + a_{n-1} x + a_n$, where $a_0 \neq 0$, n is a positive integer and a_i $(i = 0, 1, 2, \ldots n)$ are constant rationals. All the indices of x are integers and not fractions. A polynomial is, therefore, a rational algebraic expression. A polynomial has no denominators involving the variable. Hence a polynomial is sometimes called a rational integral function of the nth degree in x. For a particular value a of x,

$$f(a) = a_0 a^n + a_1 a^{n-1} + a_2 a^{n-2} + \ldots + a_{n-1} a + a_n.$$

If $f(a) = 0$, a is said to be a zero of the polynomial $f(x)$. We also say in that case that the polynomial equation $f(x) = 0$ has a root $x = a$. If we graph the curve $y = f(x)$, a zero of $f(x)$ occurs where the curve crosses the x-axis and it gives a root of the equation $f(x) = 0$. To solve such equations as well as to graph such functions, the following theorems are necessary. You are already familiar with some of them.

Theorem (*The Remainder Theorem*). If a polynomial $f(x)$ is divided by $x - r$, where r is any constant, until a constant remainder without x is obtained, this remainder is $f(r)$.

Proof: Let $q(x)$ be the quotient obtained on dividing $f(x)$ by $x - r$, and let R be the remainder. Then $f(x)$ can be expressed by the identity

$$f(x) = (x - r) \cdot q(x) + R.$$

Here $q(x)$ is polynomial of degree $n - 1$ $\ldots \ldots$ (1). Since the identity is true for all values of x it is true for $x = r$. If we substitute $x = r$ in the identity (1) above, we have $f(r) = 0 \cdot q(x) + R$.

$$\therefore f(r) = R.$$

Example 1: Find the remainder on dividing $3x^4 + 5x^3 - 7x^2 + 4x + 6$ by $x - 2$.

$$f(x) = 3x^4 + 5x^3 - 7x^2 + 4x + 6$$
$$R = f(2) = 3 \times 16 + 5 \times 8 - 7 \times 4 + 4 \times 2 + 6$$
$$= 48 + 40 - 28 + 8 + 6$$
$$= 74.$$

This can be verified by actually dividing the polynomial by $x - 2$.

$$
\begin{array}{r}
3x^3 + 11x^2 + 15x + 34 \\
x-2)\overline{\smash{)}3x^4 + 5x^3 - 7x^2 + 4x + 6} \\
3x^4 - 6x^3 \\
\hline
11x^3 - 7x^2 \\
11x^3 \quad 22x^2 \\
\hline
15x^2 + 4x \\
15x^2 - 30x \\
\hline
34x + 6 \\
34x - 68 \\
\hline
74
\end{array}
$$

7. Synthetic Division.

The process of division for polynomials can be greatly simplified when the divisor is in the form $x - r$. This process known as synthetic division is illustrated by taking the same example as above i.e. $3x^4 + 5x^3 - 7x^2 + 4x + 6$ by $x - 2$.

$$
\begin{array}{r|rrrrr}
2) & 3 & 5 & -7 & 4 & 6 \\
   &   & 6 & 22 & 30 & 68 \\
\hline
   & 3 & 11 & 15 & 34 & 74
\end{array}
$$

The first row consists of the coefficients of the polynomial in descending order. The first coefficient in the quotient is 3. Since the divisor is $x - 2$, we multiply 3 by 2 and place it in the second row below the second coefficient 5 of the first row. Adding 6 and 5, we obtain 11. This is the second coefficient in the quotient. Again multiplying 11 by 2, we place 22 below the third number in the first row. Adding the two, we obtain 15 as the third coefficient in the quotient and so on. The coefficients of the quotient are written in the third row.

The quotient is one degree lower than the given polynomial. Thus the quotient is $3x^3+11x^2+15x+34$ and the remainder is 74 (i.e. the last number in the third row). This method is simpler to use when n or r is large. It enables us to find the quotient as well as the remainder.

Example 2: Suppose we have to find the remainder $f(r)$ when $f(x)=x^3+4x^2-9$ is divided by $x+7$.

$$R=f(-7) = (-7)\,(-7)\,(-7)+4(-7)\,(-7)-9$$
$$= -49\times7+4\times49-9$$
$$= -343+196-9=-352+196=-156$$

We can find it more easily by synthetic division:

$$
\begin{array}{r|rrrr}
-7) & 1 & 4 & 0 & -9 \\
    &   & -7 & 21 & -147 \\
\hline
    & 1 & -3 & 21 & -156
\end{array}
$$

Here the remainder is the last number in the 3rd row. The quotient is $x^2-3x+21$ and $R=-156$.

The Factor Theorem. If the remainder $f(r)$ is zero, then $x-r$ is a factor of the polynomial $f(x)$.

Since r is a zero of $f(x)$, i.e. the remainder $f(r)$ is zero, if we divide $f(x)$ by $x-r$, we can write $f(x)$ in the form

$$f(x) = (x-r)\cdot q(x)+0$$
$$= (x-r)q(x).$$

$\therefore$ $x-r$ is a factor of $f(x)$.

Conversely, if $x-r$ is a factor of $f(x)$, then

$$R = f(r)=0 \text{ and } r \text{ is a zero of } f(x).$$

Given $f(x)=(x-r)\cdot q(x).$

$\therefore f(r)=0\cdot q(x)=0$

This theorem enables us to find the factors of a polynomial $f(x)$. Once the factors are known, the zeros of the polynomial $f(x)$ can be found. These zeros are the roots of the equation $f(x)=0$.

Example 3: Find whether $x-3$ is a factor of $2x^3-7x^2+9$.

$f(x)=2x^3-7x^2+9$ and $f(3)=54-63+9=0$

$\therefore$ $x-3$ is a factor. We can also check up by using synthetic division:

$$
\begin{array}{r|rrrr}
3) & 2 & -7 & 0 & 9 \\
   &   & 6 & -3 & -9 \\
\hline
   & 2 & -1 & -3 & 0
\end{array}
$$

The quotient is $2x^2-x-3$ and the remainder is 0.

Exercise 7·1

By using synthetic division, find the remainder and check by the Remainder Theorem when

1. x^3+x^2+3x-8 is divided b $x-2$.

2. $x^3-10x+5$ is divided by $x+2$.

3. $2x^3+5x^2+7x-14$ is divided by $x-1$.

4. $x^4+2x^3-3x^2+5x-10$ is divided by $x+3$.

5, $2x^4-5x+8$ is divided by $x-4$.

6. x^3-3x^2+x-3 is divided by $x+2$.

7. x^4-3x^2+6 is divided by $x-\frac{1}{2}$.

8. x^4-4x^2+3 is divided by $x-\frac{1}{3}$.

9. $2x^4+6x^3+x^2+3x-6$ is divided by $x+3$.

10. $3x^3-4x^2+8x+8$ is divided by $x+\frac{2}{3}$.

By using the Factor theorem, determine whether

11. $x-1$ is a factor of $3x^3-7x^2+5x-1$.

12. $x+3$,,   ,, $2x^3+7x^2-9$.

13. $x-3$,,   ,, $2x^3-9x^2+27$.

14. $x+1$,,   ,, $3x^3-4x^2+3x-2$.

15. $x+\frac{1}{2}$,,   ,, $4x^4-3x^3+x+1$.

16. $2x+1$,,   ,, $2x^3-5x^2+x+2$.

[*Hint*: Divide in the first instance the divisor and the dividend by 2.]

17. $x+3$ is a factor of x^5+273.

18. $2x+3$,, ,, $2x^4+3x^3+2x^2+x+1$.

19. $3x+1$,, ,, $9x^3+6x^2-7x+2$.

20. $x-y$,, ,, x^5+y^5, x^5-y^5.

7.3. The fundamental Theorem of algebra.

In the previous chapter, we have proved certain results regarding the integers based on the Euclid's Algorithm. These results can be made applicable to polynomials by the same process. Instead of $a=bq+r$, we write $f(x)=q_1(x)g(x)+r_1(x)$, where $f(x)$ is a polynomial of degree $n>0$, with rational coefficients, $g(x)$ is a similar polynomial of degree $m>0$ and $n>m$. The H.C.F. of $f(x)$ and $g(x)$ is the polynomial of highest degree which divides both. We can find it by dividing $f(x)$ by $g(x)$ by Euclid's Algorithm. We first obtain a quotient $q_1(x)$ and the remainder $r_1(x)$. Dividing $g(x)$ by $r_1(x)$, we obtain $g(x)=q_2(x)r_1(x)+r_2(x)$ and so on. Since the successive remainders are of decreasing degrees, it must happen sooner or later, that a remainder of zero degree will be obtained. As in the case of integers, we find that if $h(x)$ is the H.C.F. of $f(x)$ and $g(x)$, then there exist polynomials $\phi(x)$ and $\psi(x)$ such that $h(x)=\phi(x)f(x)+\psi(x)g(x)$ .... (1)

For instance, let $f(x)=x^4+x^2-2$ and
$g(x)=x^3+2x^2+2x+4$.

By Euclid's Algorithm, we can find their H.C.F.

$$
\begin{array}{r}
x-2 \\
x^3+2x^2+2x+4 \overline{)\,x^4+x^2-2} \\
x^4+2x^3+2x^2+4x \\
\hline
-2x^3-x^2-4x-2 \\
-2x^3-4x^2-4x-8 \\
\hline
3x^2+6
\end{array}
$$

Here $r_1(x) = 3(x^2+2)$. Ignoring the numerical factor 3, the next division will be of x^3+2x^2+2x+4 by x^2+2.

$$
\begin{array}{r}
x+2 \\
x^2+2)\ \overline{\smash{)}\ x^3+2x^2+2x+4} \\
x^3+2x \\
\hline
2x^2+4 \\
2x^2+4 \\
\hline
0
\end{array}
$$

∴ the first non-zero remainder x^2+2 is the H.C.F, $h(x)$.

Also $x^4+x^2-2 = (x-2)\ (x^3+2x^2+2x+4) + 3(x^2+2)$.

Dividing by 3

$\frac{1}{3}(x^4+x^2-2) - \frac{1}{3}(x-2)\ (x^3+2x^2+2x+4) = x^2+2$

∴ $\frac{1}{3}f(x) - \frac{1}{3}(x-2)g(x) = h(x)$

∴ $\phi(x) = \frac{1}{3}$ and $\psi(x) = -\frac{1}{3}(x-2)$ in (1) above.

Corresponding to the prime number p, we have an *irreducible* polynomial $p(x)$ in the field of rationals, if $p(x)$ is of degree >0 and has no polynomial factors with rational coefficients other than 1 and $p(x)$ itself.

Now we can prove a theorem in Algebra corresponding to the fundamental theorem of Arithmetic in the previous chapter.

Fundamental theorem of Algebra.

Every polynomial equation of degree 1 or more has at least one root (real or imaginary).

This theorem has no elementary proof and we may, therefore, assume the result. It was first proved by a great German mathematician Gauss in 1799, when he was only 22 years old. This enables us to prove the next theorem.

Every polynomial equation $f(x) = a_0x^n + a_1x^{n-1} + \ldots\ldots$ $+ a_{n-1}\ x + a_n = 0$ has exactly n roots, where $n \geqslant 1$ and $a_0 \neq 0$.

Proof: By the fundamental theorem of Algebra, the equation $f(x) = 0$ has a root r_1. Then $x - r_1$ is a factor of $f(x)$ so that

$f(x) = (x - r_1) \, q_1 \, (x)$, where $q_1(x)$ is the quotient of $f(x)$ divided by $x - r_1$.

$q_1(x) = a_0 \, x^{n-1} + \ldots\ldots$ so that it is of degree $n - 1$.

If $n - 1 > 0$, $q_1 \, (x) = 0$ has a root r_2 by the fundamental theorem so that $q_1(x) = (x - r_2) q_2(x)$.

$\therefore f(x) = (x - r_1) \, (x - r_2) q_2(x)$.

This process can be carried on until the quotient $q_n \, (x) = a_0$ of degree 0 is reached.

$\therefore f(x) = a_0 \, (x - r_1) \, (x - r_2) \ldots. (x - r_n)$.

No value of x other than r_1, $r_2 \ldots\ldots r_n$ will make $f(x)$ zero.

$\therefore f(x) = 0$ has exactly n roots.

The equation $(x - 2)^2 \, (x + 3) \, (x - 4) \, (x - 5)^2 = 0$ is a polynomial equation of the 6th degree. Its 6 roots are 2, 2, -3, 4, 5, 5. Note that any root which occurs twice or three times is counted twice or three times. It will be regarded as a double root or a treble root.

Exercise 7.2

By means of the Euclid's Algorithm, find the H.C.F. of each of the following pairs of polynomials:

1. $x^2 + 3x + 2$, $x^3 - x^2 - 4x + 4$.

2. $x^2 + 2x + 1$, $x^2 - 1$.

3. $x^2 - x - 2$, $x^3 + 4x^2 - 4x - 16$.

4. $x^3 - x^2 + x - 1$, $x^4 + 3x^2 + 2$.

5. $x^3 + 2x^2 + 2x + 1$, $x^4 + x^2 + 1$.

6. $x^4 + x^2 + 1$, $x^5 - x^4 + x^3 + x^2 - x + 1$.

7. Show that $x - 2$ is the H.C.F. of $x^2 - 4$ and $x^2 - 5x + 6$ and if $x - 2 = (x^2 - 4) \, \phi(x) + (x^2 - 5x + 6) \, \psi(x)$, find $\phi(x)$ and $\psi(x)$.

8. Find the H.C.F. of $x^4 + 3x^2 + 2$, $x^3 - x^2 + 2x - 2$ and express it in the form $\phi(x) \, (x^4 + 3x^2 + 2) + \psi \, (x) \, (x^3 - x^2 + 2x - 2)$.

9. Find the H.C.F. of $f(x) \equiv x^4 + x^3 + 4x^2 + 3x + 3$, and
$g(x) \equiv 2x^3 + 5x^2 + 6x + 15$.
Express it in the form
$\phi(x) f(x) + \psi(x) \, g(x)$.

10. Find the H.C.F. of x^4-x^3+x-1 and x^3-x^2+x-1 and show that it can be expressed in the form

$\phi(x)\ (x^4-x^3+x-1)+\psi(x)\ (x^3-x^2+x-1)$ where

$\phi(x)=\frac{1}{2}(x+1)$ and $\psi(x)=-\frac{1}{2}(x^2+x-1)$.

7.4. Theory of equations.

(*i*) *Rational roots.*

Theorem: If the rational number p/q (p and q having no common factors) is a root of the equation

$$a_0x^n+a_1x^{n-1}+a_2x^{n-1}+\ \ldots\ +a_{n-1}x+a_n=0$$

(where a_0, a_1, a_2, etc. are integral coefficients), then p is an exact divisor of a_n and q is an exact divisor of a_o.

Proof: Since p/q is a root,

$$a_0\left(\frac{p}{q}\right)^n+a_1\left(\frac{p}{q}\right)^{n-1}+\ \ldots\ldots\ +a_{n-1}\left(\frac{p}{q}\right)+a_n=0$$

or $a_0p^n+a_1p^{n-1}q+a_2p^{n-2}q^2+\ \ldots\ldots\ +a_{n-1}pq^{n-1}+a_nq^n=0$.

Dividing by p we have

$$a_0p^{n-1}+a_1p^{n-2}q+\ \ldots\ldots\ +a_{n-1}q^{n-1}=\frac{-a_nq^n}{p}.$$

Since a_0, a_1 ...... and p and q are all integers, the left side is a sum of integers.

∴ the right side is also an integer.

This is possible if and only if p is an exact divisor of a_n. Similarly by considering the equation

$a_nq^n+a_{n-1}\ q\ q^{n-1}+\ \ldots\ldots\ +a_0p^n=0$ and dividing by q,

$$-\frac{a_0p^n}{q}\ \text{must be an integer.}$$

∴ q is an exact divisor of a_0.

As a corollary, any rational root of $x^n+a_1n^{n-1}+\ \ldots\ +a_n=0$ must be an exact divisor of the last term a_n.

(ii) *Imaginary roots.*

The roots of a quadratic equation are both real or both imaginary. If $p+iq$ is a root, its conjugate $p-iq$ is also a root. The root of general quadratic equation are

$$=\frac{-b+\sqrt{b^2-4ac}}{2a} \quad \text{and} \quad =\frac{-b-\sqrt{b^2-4ac}}{2a}.$$

If $p=-\dfrac{b}{2a}$ and $q=\dfrac{\sqrt{4ac-b^2}}{2a}$ where $b^2<4ac$,

the roots are $p+iq$ and $p-iq$. They are conjugate complex numbers.

This result applies to all equations with real coefficients no matter what the degree. This is proved below.

7.5. *Theorem:* If all the coefficients of a polynomial equation $f(x)=0$ are real and $a+ib(b\neq0)$ is an imaginary root, then its conjugate $a-ib$ is also a root.

Proof: Since $a+ib$ is a root, $[x-(a+ib)]$ is a factor of $f(x)$. If $[x-(a-ib)]$ is also a root of $f(x)=0$, then $[x-(a-ib)][x-(a+ib)]$ is a factor of $f(x)$.

But $[x-(a-ib)][x-(a-ib)]=(x-a)^2+b^2=x^2-2ax+a^2+b^2$. Now we show that $x^2-2ax+a^2+b^2$ is a factor of $f(x)$.

Let $f(x)=(x^2-2ax+a^2+b^2)\,q(x)+R(x)$ ....(1)
where $R(x)$ is the remainder, after dividing $f(x)$ by $x^2-2ax+a^2+b^2$. The remainder $R(x)$ is of degree not greater than 1, as the divisor is of the second degree. Let $R(x)$ be $cx+d$. Since the coefficients of $f(x)$ and of the divisor are all real, the quotient and the remainder must have also real coefficients.

Now substituting $x=a+ib$ in the result (1),
$f(a+ib) = 0 \cdot q(a+ib)+R(a+ib)$ and
$0 = c(a+ib)+d=ca+d+ibc$.
This is possible if and only if $bc=0$ and $ca+d=0$.

Since $b\neq0$, $c=0$. $\therefore d=0$. $\therefore c(a-ib)+d=0$.
Hence $f(a-ib)=0$.
$\therefore f(x)$ has $a-ib$ also as one of its factors.

Corollary: Every polynomial $f(x)$ of degree >1 can be expressed as a product of linear facorts and quadratic factors (whose discriminants are negative).

For, $f(x) = a_0 (x - r_1) (x - r_2) \ldots \ldots (x - r_n)$.
If a root r_i is an imaginary number $a + i\beta$, there must be another root r_j which is an imaginary number $a - i\beta$.

$\therefore (x - r_i) (x - r_j) = x^2 - 2ax + a^2 + \beta^2$ which is a quadratic factor of $f(x)$. The discriminant of this quadratic expression is $4a^2 - 4(a^2 + \beta^2)$ or $-4\beta^2$. Since β is a real number, the discriminant is negative.

(iii) *Theorem:* If $f(x)$ with rational coefficients has a surd root of the form $a + \sqrt{b}$ where a and b are rational, then the conjugate surd $a - \sqrt{b}$ is also a root.

The proof is similar to that of theorem ii.

A cubic equation or a polynomial equation of an odd degree with real coefficients cannot have all imaginary roots. For, the imaginary roots occur in conjugate pairs. A cubic equation has only three roots. All the three roots may be real or one real and two imaginary. Similarly a cubic equation with rational coefficients cannot have all surd roots.

Example 4: Find the roots of $f(x) = 4x^4 - 7x^2 - 5x - 1 = 0$.

Here all the coefficients of the quartic equation are real and rational.

The rational root $\dfrac{p}{q}$ must be such that p is a divisor of -1 and q is a divisor of 4.

$\therefore$ the possible rational roots are $\pm \frac{1}{4}, \pm \frac{1}{2}, \pm 1$.
By substituting, it is easy to see that ± 1 arc not roots.

We can verify whether $\frac{1}{4}$ or $-\frac{1}{4}$ is a root by either substituting $x = \pm \frac{1}{4}$ or by carrying out synthetic division. Let us try $\frac{1}{4}$.

$$f(\tfrac{1}{4}) = 4 \cdot \tfrac{1}{4_4} - 7 \cdot \tfrac{1}{4_2} - \tfrac{5}{4} - 1 = \tfrac{1}{64} - \tfrac{7}{16} - \tfrac{5}{4} - 1$$
$$= \frac{1-28-80-64}{64}$$

This is not zero.   We can see that $x = -\tfrac{1}{4}$ also will not do.
Let us try $\tfrac{1}{2}$.

$$f(\tfrac{1}{2}) = 4 \cdot \tfrac{1}{16} - \tfrac{7}{4} - \tfrac{5}{2} - 1 = \tfrac{1}{4} - \tfrac{7}{4} - \tfrac{5}{2} - 1$$

This will not do.

Now let us try $-\tfrac{1}{2}$.

$$f(-\tfrac{1}{2}) = \tfrac{1}{4} - \tfrac{7}{4} + \tfrac{5}{2} - 1 = 0$$

$\therefore$ $x + \tfrac{1}{2}$ or $2x+1$ is a factor of the given equation. This can
be seen from the synthetic division too.

$$
\begin{array}{r|rrrr}
-\tfrac{1}{2}) & 4 & 0 & -7 & -5 & -1 \\
 & & -2 & 1 & 3 & 1 \\
\hline
 & 4 & -2 & -6 & -2 & 0
\end{array}
$$

The quotient is $4x^3 - 2x^2 - 6x - 2$ and the remainder is 0.

$\therefore$ $x + \tfrac{1}{2}$ or $2x+1$ is a factor of the given equation.

$\therefore$ $4x^4 - 7x^2 - 5x - 1 = (x + \tfrac{1}{2})\ (4x^3 - 2x^2 - 6x - 2)$
$$= (2x+1)\ (2x^3 - x^2 - 3x - 1)$$

Now we have reduced the given equation by one degree by
dividing it by $2x+1$.   Now we can deal with $2x^3 - x^2 - 3x - 1$
$=0$, which is easier than the given equation.   This equation
is called the *depressed equation*.   Trying $x = -\tfrac{1}{2}$ again,

$$
\begin{array}{r|rrr}
-\tfrac{1}{2}) & 2 & -1 & -3 & -1 \\
 & & -1 & 1 & 1 \\
\hline
 & 2 & -2 & -2 & 0
\end{array}
$$

$\therefore$ $2x+1$ is again a factor.

$\therefore (2x^3 - x^2 - 3x - 1) = (2x+1)\ (x^2 - x - 1)$

$\therefore f(x) = (2x+1)^2\ (x^2 - x - 1)$.

$\therefore$ the roots required are $-\tfrac{1}{2}, -\tfrac{1}{2}, \dfrac{1+\sqrt{5}}{2}$ and $\dfrac{1-\sqrt{5}}{2}$.

$-\tfrac{1}{2}$ is a double root.

Example 5: Find the roots of the equation

$$8x^5-12x^4+14x^3-13x^2+6x-1=0.$$

The possible rational roots are ±1, $\pm\frac{1}{2}$, $\pm\frac{1}{4}$, $\pm\frac{1}{8}$. Since the signs of the terms of the equations alternate, there are no negative roots. For, by substituting them, all the terms will be negative and will not make R zero. Let us try $x=\frac{1}{2}$.

$$
\begin{array}{r|rrrrrr}
\tfrac{1}{2}) & 8 & -12 & 14 & -13 & 6 & -1 \\
  &   & 4 & -4 & 5 & -4 & 1 \\
\hline
  & 8 & -8 & 10 & -8 & 2 & 0
\end{array}
$$

$\therefore$ $x-\frac{1}{2}$ or $2x-1$ is a factor of the given equation.

The depressed equation after dividing the given equation by $x-\frac{1}{2}$ is $8x^4-8x^3+10x^2-8x+2=0$ or

$$4x^4-4x^3+5x^2-4x+1=0$$

This equation may also have $\frac{1}{2}$, $\frac{1}{4}$ as roots.

Trying this, we see that $\frac{1}{2}$ is a root of this equation too.

$$
\begin{array}{r|rrrrr}
\tfrac{1}{2}) & 4 & -4 & 5 & -4 & 1 \\
  &   & 2 & -1 & 2 & -1 \\
\hline
  & 4 & -2 & 4 & -2 & 0
\end{array}
$$

$\therefore$ $\frac{1}{2}$ is a root of the depressed equation and dividing it by $x-\frac{1}{2}$, we see that $4x^3-2x^2+4x-2=0$ is the next depressed equation. Dividing by the common factor 2, we have

$2x^3-x^2+2x-1=0$ is the next depressed equation. Trying $\frac{1}{2}$ as a root again, we have by synthetic division

$$
\begin{array}{r|rrrr}
\tfrac{1}{2}) & 2 & -1 & 2 & -1 \\
  &   & 1 & 0 & 1 \\
\hline
  & 2 & 0 & 2 & 0
\end{array}
$$

$\therefore$ $\frac{1}{2}$ is the root of the depressed equation and

$2x^2+2=0$ or $x^2+1=0$ is the next depressed equation. The roots of this are $\pm i$.

$\therefore$ the roots required are $\frac{1}{2}$, $\frac{1}{2}$, $\frac{1}{2}$, $\pm i$

We note that $\frac{1}{2}$ is a multiple root, as it occurs three times.

Example 6 : Find the roots of $6x^4+7x^3+5x^2-x-2=0$.

The last term 2 has factors ±1 and ±2 and the first term 6 has factors, 1, 2, 3, 6

$\therefore$ the possible roots are ±1, $\pm\frac{1}{2}$, $\pm\frac{1}{3}$, $\pm\frac{2}{3}$, ±2.

By substituting $x=\pm1$, we easily see that they are not the roots. Let us try $\frac{1}{2}$.

$$
\begin{array}{r|rrrrr}
\frac{1}{2}) & 6 & 7 & 5 & -1 & -2 \\
& & 3 & 5 & 5 & 2 \\
\hline
& 6 & 10 & 10 & 4 & 0
\end{array}
$$

$\therefore$ $-\frac{1}{2}$ is a root i.e. $2x+1$ is a factor and the depressed equation is $6x^3+10x^2+10x+4=0$

i.e. $3x^3+5x^2+5x+2=0$.

The possible roots of the depressed equation are $\pm\frac{2}{3}$, $\pm\frac{1}{3}$, ±2.

Since all the signs are positive, 2, $+\frac{1}{3}$ and $+\frac{2}{3}$ are to be left out of consideration; for, they will make the expression positive.

Let us try $-\frac{2}{3}$

$$
\begin{array}{r|rrrr}
-\frac{2}{3}) & 6 & 10 & 10 & 4 \\
& & -4 & -4 & -4 \\
\hline
& 6 & 6 & 6 & 0
\end{array}
$$

Here $R=0$ and so $-\frac{2}{3}$ is a root.

$\therefore$ the next depressed equation is $6x^2+6x+6=0$ or $x^2+x+1=0$. The roots of the quadratic equation are

$$\frac{-1\pm\sqrt{1-4}}{2}=\frac{-1\pm\sqrt{3}i}{2}$$

$\therefore$ the roots of $f(x)=0$ are $\frac{1}{2}$, $\dfrac{-2}{3}$ and $\dfrac{-1\pm\sqrt{3}i}{2}$

Example 7 : Solve the equation $x^3-\frac{5}{2}x^2-5x+\frac{3}{2}=0$.

The equation in integral coefficients becomes

$2x^3-5x^2-10x+3=0$

The possible roots are $\pm(1, \frac{1}{2}, \frac{3}{2}, 3)$. ±1 are easily seen to be not the roots. Similarly $\pm\frac{1}{2}$ are also not the roots. Trying $-\frac{3}{2}$

$$-\frac{3}{2}) \quad \begin{array}{cccc} 1 & -\frac{5}{2} & -5 & +\frac{3}{2} \\ & -\frac{3}{2} & 6 & -\frac{3}{2} \\ \hline 1 & -4 & 1 & 0 \end{array}$$

Here $R=0$. $\therefore$ $-\frac{3}{2}$ is a root.

The depressed equation is $x^2-4x+1=0$

The roots are $\dfrac{4\pm\sqrt{4^2-4}}{2} = 2\pm\sqrt{3}$

$\therefore$ the roots are $-\frac{3}{2}$, $2+\sqrt{3}$ and $2-\sqrt{3}$.

Exercise 7·3

Find the roots of the following equations:

1. $x^3-19x-30=0$.

2. $x^3-3x^2-24x+80=0$.

3. $x^3-4x^2+x+6=0$.

4. $x^3+4x^2+8x+8=0$.

5. $x^4+x^3+34x^2+36x-72=0$.

6. $x^4-x^3-7x^2+x+6=0$.

7. $x^4+2x^3-17x^2-18x+72=0$.

8. $x^4+x^3+32x^2-4x-144=0$.

9. $x^4-3x^3+x^2+4=0$.

10. $x^4-x^3-19x^2+49x-30=0$.

11. $2x^3+5x^2-x-1=0$.

12. $2x^3-8x^2-x+4=0$.

13. $2x^3-3x^2-11x+6=0$.

14. $12x^3-52x^2+61x-15=0$.

15. $4x^4-7x^2-5x-1=0$.

16. $4x^4-12x^3+13x^2-12x+9=0$

17. $x^4-\frac{1}{2}x^3+x^2-2x-12=0$.

18. $4x^4-4x^3+13x^2-12x+3=0$.

19. $6x^4-13x^3-23x^2+39x+15=0$.

20. $x^4+\frac{25}{6}x^3+\frac{25}{3}x^2+\frac{17}{2}x+3=0$.

21. $x^4-x^3-7x^2-14x-24=0$.

22. $2x^4+x^3-2x^2-4x-3=0$.

23. $4x^4+8x^3-7x^2-21x-9=0$.

24. $4x^5-16x^4+17x^3-19x^2+13x-3=0$.

25. $3x^5+2x^4+9x^3+6x^2-12x-8=0$.

7.5. Graphs of polynomial functions.

Using the rectangular coordinate system, we are able to exhibit the association between x and the function of x which we may denote by y. By using synthetic division for any value of the variable x, a table of values of y (i.e. the polynomial function here) can be constructed and the graph may be sketched. The roots of a polynomial equation are given by the abscissae of the points where the graph of the function $y = f(x)$ crosses or touches the x-axis. The student is familiar with the elementary polynomial functions—linear and quadratic functions.

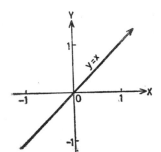

$y = x$ is a straight line bisecting the x and y axes. The general linear function is $y = ax + b$.

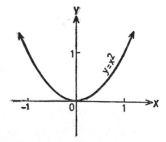

$y = x^2$ represents a parabola. It is symmetrical about the y-axis.

$y=ax^2+bx+c$ is the general quadratic function and the shape of the curve is the same as $y=x^2$.

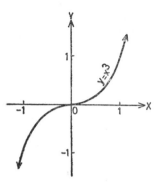

This is the cubical curve, $y=x^3$. It is called cubical parabola. All the three roots of the equation $x^3=0$ are at the centre i.e. $x=0$. The curve touches and crosses the x-axis at the origin 0. Such a point is called a *point of inflexion.*

The general cubic equation is $y=ax^3+bx^2+cx+d$. The graph of a cubic equation may cut the x-axis at three points or only at one point. That means that there can be three real roots of the general cubic equation, $ax^3+bx^2+cx+d=0$ or may have only one real root. In the latter case the equation has two imaginary roots. The point at which the curve cuts the x-axis may be a double or a treble point.

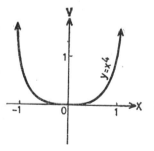

This is the quartic curve $y=x^4$. It is somewhat flat at the bottom and the x-axis is the tangent at the origin. The general quartic equation is $y=ax^4+bx^3+cx^2+dx+e$.

The graph of this curve may cut the x-axis in four points in which case the quartic equation $ax^4+bx^3+cx^2+dx+e=0$

will have four real roots or may have a multiple point on the x-axis, like a double or treble point. The quartic may cut the x-axis only at two points or one double point in which case the other two roots are imaginary. It may not cut the x-axis at any point in which case all the four roots are imaginary.

One of the methods of finding the roots of a polynomial equation is to construct the graph of the polynomial on the Oxy plane. When the curve cuts the x-axis, the x-coordinate of each such point gives a root of the equation. It is not always easy to draw the graph of a polynomial function. One has to have a good deal of practice in tracing such curves. The following points are worth-noting:

First construct a table of convenient values of x and y. Usually it is wise to use integral values of x in a certain interval. Then plot the points. It will make for convenience, if you equate the derivative of the polynomial to zero. Those points give the turning points of the curve corresponding to the maximum and minimum values of the function. There may be points of inflexion also. The method will be clear by studying the following graphs:

Example 1: Trace the curve $y=x^3-2x^2+1$. The following table gives a few approximate values of y for $-1 \leqslant x \leqslant 2$.

x	-1	$-.8$	$-.6$	$-.4$	$-.2$	0	$.2$	$.4$	$.6$	1	1.2	1.4	2
y	-2	$-.8$	$.06$	$.6$	$.9$	1	$.9$	$.7$	$.5$	0	$-.15$	$-.08$	1

The three roots of the equation $x^3-2x^2+1=0$ are $-.6$, 1, 1.6. The first and the third roots are only approximate, the actual roots being $-\dfrac{\sqrt{5}-1}{2}$ and $\dfrac{\sqrt{5}+1}{2}$ respectively. All the three roots are real.

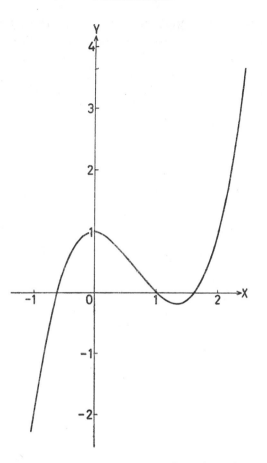

Example 2 : Draw the graph of the function $x^3 - 5x^2 + 7x - 3$. The table of values of y for x between -1 and 4 is given below:

x	-1	$-\cdot4$	0	$\cdot2$	$\cdot4$	1	1.2	1.6	2	2.6	3	4
y	-16	$-6\cdot7$	-3	$-1\cdot8$	$-\cdot99$	0	$-\cdot07$	$-\cdot5$	-1	-1	0	9

For turning points $3x^2-10x+7=0$ i.e. $(3x-7)(x-1)=0$
$\therefore$ $x=1$ gives the maximum value of the function, as $f''(x)=6x-10$ and is $-$ve at $x=1$. The curve touches the x-axis at 1. The minimum value is given by $x=\frac{7}{3}$, as $f''(x)$ is positive for this value. The roots are 1, 1, 3. The shape of the curve is as under:

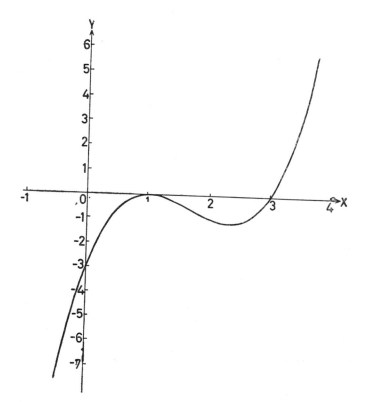

Example 3: Solve graphically the equation $x^3-6x+9=0$.

Since we have to draw the graph of $y=x^3-6x+9$, we first construct a table of values of x and y.

x	-4	-3	-2	-1	0	1	2	3
y	-31	0	13	14	9	4	5	18

The function is negative for all $x < -3$ and positive for all other values of x.

The derivative $3x^2 - 6$ is zero for $x = \pm\sqrt{2}$.

∴ the turning values of y are at points $x = \sqrt{2}$ and $-\sqrt{2}$. From the values of y in the table, it is clear that the function

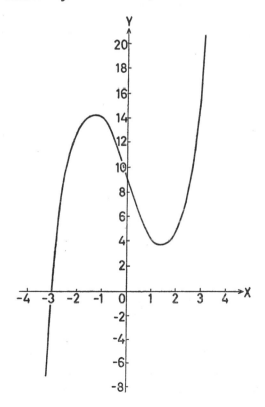

goes on increasing up to $x=-\sqrt{2}$ and then decreases up to $x=\sqrt{2}$. Then it goes up again sharply, $y=14\cdot6$ for $x=-\sqrt{2}$ and $3\cdot4$ for $x=\sqrt{2}$ approximately. Now we are in a position to trace the curve.

The curve crosses the x-axis at only one point $x=-3$. Hence the only real root of the given equation is -3, the other two roots being imaginary.

Example 4: Trace the curve $y=x^4-3x^3+x^2+3x-2$.

The function y here is a polynomial of the fourth degree and by sketching its curve, we obtain a quartic curve.

x	-2	$-1\cdot2$	-1	0	$\cdot5$	1	$1\cdot5$	2	3	$-\cdot8$
y	36	$3\cdot1$	0	-2	$-\cdot6$	0	$-\cdot3$	0	16	$-1\cdot8$

The turning points of the curve are given by
$$4x^3-9x^2+2x+3=0 \text{ i.e. } (x-1)(4x^2-5x-3)=0.$$

$\therefore$ turning points occur at $x=1$ and $x=\dfrac{5\pm\sqrt{73}}{8}$, the last two of which are approximately equal to $x=1\cdot7$ and $x=-0\cdot4$. The curve can now be traced.

At the turning points, $x=1$, $y=0$, $x=1\cdot7$, $y=-\cdot4$ and $x=-\cdot4$, $y=-2\cdot8$, the last two being approximate.

The x-axis is tangent to the curve at $x=1$. The curve cuts the x-axis at -1, 1 and 2. $x=1$ is a double root of the quartic equation.

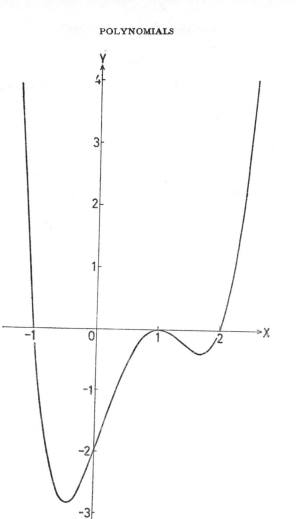

Example 5: Trace the quartic curve $y=x^4+3x^3+3x^2+x$ or $y=x(x+1)^3$.

The roots are obviously 0 and -1, the last one being a triple root.

We construct a table of values of x and y.

x	-2	$-1{\cdot}8$	$-1{\cdot}6$	$-1{\cdot}4$	$-1{\cdot}2$	-1	$-{\cdot}4$	$-{\cdot}2$	0	${\cdot}2$	${\cdot}4$	1
y	2	${\cdot}92$	${\cdot}35$	${\cdot}09$	${\cdot}01$	0	$-{\cdot}09$	$-{\cdot}1$	0	${\cdot}35$	$1{\cdot}1$	8

The derivative $4x^3+9x^2+6x+1$ is zero at the turning points. $4x^3+9x^2+6x+1=(4x+1)(x+1)^2$ so that at $x=-1$, the curve crosses the x-axis and bends away in opposite directions, as it is a point of inflexion. At $x=-\frac{1}{4}$, the curve has a minimum value $-{\cdot}1$; the function decreases in value from $x=-1$ to $x=-\frac{1}{4}$ and from there it rises sharply.

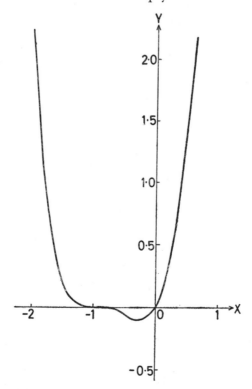

Exercise 7.4.

Draw the graphs of the following functional equations, showing the location of all the real roots:

1. $y=-x^3$.   **2.** $y=x^3+1$.   **3.** $y=x^2+x+1$.

4. $y=x^3-x+1$.   **5.** $y=x^3-x^2-2x+1$.

6. $y=x^3-3x^2+x-3$.   **7.** $y=x^3-3x+1$.

8. $y=x^4-4x^3+x^2+6x+2$.   **9.** $y=x^4-4x^3+6x^2-8x+8$.

10. $y=x^4+x^2+1$. **11.** $y=x^4-x^2+1$. **12.** $y=x^4-x^3-x^2-2x-6$.

7.6. Coefficients and roots.

As we have seen earlier, the coefficients of a polynomial determine the nature of the polynomial. They determine the roots of the polynomial equation. It is, therefore, natural to expect the existence of some definite relationship between the coefficients and the roots. Let the polynomial equation be

$$a_0 x^n + a_1 x^{n-1} + \ldots + a_n = 0 \ldots \ldots (1).$$

If this equation has roots $r_1, r_2, \ldots \ldots r_n$, the equation (1) can be written also as $a_0(x-r_1)(x-r_2) \ldots \ldots (x-r_n) = 0$ $\ldots \ldots (2)$

Dividing (1) and (2) by a_0, we have

$$x^n + \frac{a_1 x^{n-1}}{a_0} + \frac{a_2 x^{n-2}}{a_0} + \ldots \ldots + \frac{a_n}{a_0} = (x-r_1)(x-r_2)$$
$$\ldots \ldots (x-r_n)$$
$$= x^n - (r_1+r_2+r_3+ \ldots \ldots +r_n)x^{n-1} + (r_1r_2+r_1r_3+ \ldots)x^{n-2}$$
$$-(r_1r_2r_3+r_1r_2r_4+ \ldots)x^{n-3} + \ldots \ldots + (-1)^n r_1r_2r_3\ldots r_n.$$

Comparing the coefficients of x^n, x^{n-1}, x^{n-2} etc. in (1) and (2), we have the sum of the roots $r_1+r_2+ \ldots \ldots +r_n = -\frac{a_1}{a_0}$, the sum of all possible products of the roots taken two at a time

i.e. $\Sigma r_i r_j \ (i \neq j) = \frac{a_2}{a_0}$,

the sum of all possible products of the roots taken three at a time i.e. $\Sigma r_i r_j r_k \ (i \neq j \neq k) = -\dfrac{a_3}{a_0}$ and so on until we come to $r_1 r_2 r_3 \ \ldots . \ r_n = \dfrac{(-1)^n \ a_n}{a_0}$. For instance, the quartic equation $x^4 + 5x^3 + 5x^2 - 5x - 6 = 0$ has four roots $r_1 = 1$, $r_2 = -1$, $r_3 = -2$, $r_4 = -3$.

Now the sum of the roots $= \Sigma r = -5$ which is true as
$-3 - 2 - 1 + 1 = -5$.

$\Sigma r_1 r_2 = 5$ which is also true as $(-3) \ (-2) +$
$(-3) \ (-1) + (-3) \ (1) + (-2) \ (-1) + (-2) \ (1) + (-1)(1)$
$= 6 + 3 - 3 + 2 - 2 - 1 = 5$.

$\Sigma r_1 r_2 r_3 = -(-5)$ or 5 which can be verified by actual multiplication, $(1) \ (-1) \ (-2) + (1) \ (-1) \ (-3)$
$+ (1) \ (-2) \ (-3) + (-1) \ (-2) \ (-3) = 2 + 3 + 6 - 6 = 5$.

And $r_1 r_2 r_3 r_4 = -6$, which is actually the case as
$(1) \ (-1) \ (-2) \ (-3) = -6$

Example: Find the value of k so that one root is the negative of another for the equation $2x^3 + 3x^2 + kx - 3 = 0$ and solve the equation.

If $r_1 = -r_2$, $r_1 + r_2 = 0$.   Now $r_1 + r_2 + r_3 = -\frac{3}{2}$.

$\therefore r_3 = -\frac{3}{2}$.   Substituting this value for x in the equation,
$-\frac{27}{4} + \frac{27}{4} - \frac{3}{2}k - 3 = 0$

$\therefore k = -2$. $\therefore$ the equation is
$2x^3 + 3x^2 - 2x - 3 = 0$. $r_1 r_2 r_3 = \frac{3}{2} r^2_1 = \frac{3}{2}$ $\therefore r^2_1 = 1$ or
$r_1 = \pm 1$.

$\therefore 1, \ -1, \ -\frac{3}{2}$ are the roots.

Example: Find the value of $r^2_1 + r^2_2 + r^2_3 + r^2_4$ where r_1, r_2 etc. are the roots of the quartic equation $x^4 - 3x^3 + x^2 - 5x + 2 = 0$.

The sum of the roots $r_1 + r_2 + r_3 + r_4 = 3$, as the coefficients of x^3 is -3 and $\Sigma r_1 r_2 = 1$ as the coefficient of x^2 is 1.

$\therefore (r_1 + r_2 + r_3 + r_4)^2 = \Sigma r^2_1 + 2 \Sigma r_1 r_2$
$\therefore 9 = \Sigma r^2 + 2$
$\therefore \Sigma r^2 = 7$.

Exercise 7.5.

1. Find the sum and product of the roots of $2x^3+x^2-8x-4=0$. Find the actual roots and verify your result.

2. Solve the equation $x^3-3x^2+kx+3=0$, given that one root is the negative of another.

3. Find the value of k and solve the equation $x^3+2x^2+kx-6=0$, given that the sum of two of the roots is -4.

4. Find the value of k and solve the equation $x^4-2x^3-11x^2+kx+36$, given that there are two distinct double roots which are real.

5. If $x^4+ax^3-13x^2+bx+36=0$ has four roots α, β, $-\alpha$, $-\beta$, find them and the values of a and b.

6. Find the values of h and k and solve the equation $x^3+hx+k=0$ given that one root is 3 and the difference between the other roots is one.

7. Show that if α, β, γ, δ are the roots of the quartic equation $x^4+ax^3+bx^2+cx+d=0$, $dx^4+cx^3+bx^2+ax+1=0$ has $\dfrac{1}{\alpha}$, $\dfrac{1}{\beta}$, $\dfrac{1}{\gamma}$, $\dfrac{1}{\delta}$ as its roots. [*Hint*: Replace x by $\dfrac{1}{x}$ in the first equation.]

8. Show that if one root of $x^3+bx^2+cx+d=0$ is the negative of another, then $d=bc$.

9. Prove that if α, β, γ are the roots of the cubic equation $x^3+ax^2+bx+c=0$ such that $\dfrac{1}{\alpha}+\dfrac{1}{\beta}+\dfrac{1}{\gamma}=0$, then $b=0$.

10. Find h and k and solve the equation $2x^3-11x^2+hx+k=0$, given that $-\frac{1}{2}$ is the first root and the third root is twice the second.

11. If r_1, r_2, r_3, r_4 are the roots of $3x^4-2x^3-5x^2+7x-6=0$, find the value of $\overset{4}{\underset{1}{\Sigma}}\ r_n^2$.

12. If r_1, r_2, r_3, r_4 are the roots of $2x^4-13x^3+21x^2-2x-8=0$, find the value of $\overset{4}{\underset{1}{\Sigma}}\dfrac{1}{r_n^2}$ [see ex. 7 above.]

CHAPTER 8

Matrices and Determinants

8.1. A matrix.

It is often convenient in Mathematics to consider an ordered set of $m \times n$ elements, arranged in an array of m rows and n columns, where m and n are given integers. This array o numbers is called a *matrix*. For instance,

$\begin{bmatrix} a_1 & b_1 & c_1 \\ a_2 & b_2 & c_2 \end{bmatrix}$ is a matrix of two rows and three columns.

The numbers a_1, b_1, c_1, a_2, b_2, c_2 are called *elements* of the matrix. The horizontal lines of numbers are called rows, while the vertical lines of numbers are called columns. A matrix does not stand for any particular value of numbers. It is a complex of values indicated in a particular way, viz. in m rows and n columns. Sometimes a matrix is indicated merely by one letter written in bold type, say **A**. Sometimes, the elements are spelled out in their $m \times n$ array and bordered by double vertical lines or enclosed by brackets. For example,

$$A = \begin{Vmatrix} 2 & 3 \\ 1 - 7 \\ 3 & 1 \end{Vmatrix} = \begin{pmatrix} 2 & 3 \\ 1 - 7 \\ 3 & 1 \end{pmatrix} = \begin{bmatrix} 2 & 3 \\ 1 - 7 \\ 3 & 1 \end{bmatrix}$$

We shall use the latter notation in this book for a matrix. In A, the elements are not indicated while they are in the other notations.

A general matrix of m rows and n columns is known as $m \times n$ matrix and is written

$$\begin{vmatrix} a_{11} & a_{12} & a_{13} & \cdots & a_{1j} & \cdots & a_{1n} \\ a_{21} & a_{22} & a_{23} & \cdots & a_{2j} & \cdots & a_{2n} \\ \cdots\cdots\cdots\cdots\cdots\cdots\cdots\cdots\cdots\cdots\cdots \\ a_{i1} & a_{i2} & a_{i3} & & a_{ij} & & a_{in} \\ \cdots\cdots\cdots\cdots\cdots\cdots\cdots\cdots\cdots\cdots\cdots \\ a_{m1} & a_{m2} & a_{m3} & \cdots & a_{mj} & \cdots & a_{mn} \end{vmatrix}$$

This may be simply written $\| a_{ij} \|$ in which only one typical element of ith row and j^{th} column is shown. The number of rows (i.e. m) multiplied by the number of columns (i.e. n) indicates the type of the matrix. When $m=n$, then the matrix is a square matrix whereas, when m and n are different, it is a rectangular matrix.

Case 1: $m=n=1$. The matrix has a single element denoted by $[a]$.

Case 2: $m=2$, $n=1$, or $m=1$, $n=2$ or $m=n=2$

$$\begin{bmatrix} a \\ b \end{bmatrix}$$ Here $m=2$, $n=1$.

$[a \quad b]$ Here $m=1$ and $n=2$.

$$\begin{bmatrix} a & b \\ c & d \end{bmatrix}$$ Here $m=2$ and $n=2$. It is a square matrix.

Generally a $1 \times n$ matrix viz. $[a_1 \, a_2 \ldots\ldots a_n]$ is called a row vector and a $m \times 1$ matrix

viz. $$\begin{bmatrix} a_1 \\ a_2 \\ \cdot\cdot \\ \cdot\cdot \\ a_m \end{bmatrix}$$ is called a *column vector*.

The array $$\begin{bmatrix} x \\ y \\ z \end{bmatrix}$$ is a matrix with 3 rows and one column. It is called a column vector with 3 rows.

There are two particular matrices of a given order which need to be mentioned separately—one is the *zero* matrix and other is the *unit* matrix.

Zero matrix is a matrix consisting of 0^s only as its elements. For example, $\begin{bmatrix} 0 & 0 & 0 \\ 0 & 0 & 0 \end{bmatrix}$ is a zero matrix of order 2×3 and is denoted by 0_{23}.

Unit matrix is an $n \times n$ matrix consisting of a diagonal with 1 as its elements and of 0^s as the other elements for all positive integral values of n. For example $\begin{bmatrix} 1 & 0 \\ 0 & 1 \end{bmatrix}$, $\begin{bmatrix} 1 & 0 & 0 \\ 0 & 1 & 0 \\ 0 & 0 & 1 \end{bmatrix}$

and $\begin{bmatrix} 1 & 0 & 0 & 0 \\ 0 & 1 & 0 & 0 \\ 0 & 0 & 1 & 0 \\ 0 & 0 & 0 & 1 \end{bmatrix}$ are unit matrices of order $2 \times 2, 3 \times 3$ and 4×4 respectively.

Definition : We say that two matrices are of the *same size* if and only if they have the same number of rows and the same number of columns. Two matrices are equal if and only if they are of the same size and all their corresponding elements are equal. This means that two equal matrices A and B are of the same size and $a_{ij} = b_{ij}$ for each i and j. In such a case, A and B denote the same matrix. For example if

$$\begin{bmatrix} x \\ y \\ z \end{bmatrix} = \begin{bmatrix} 1 \\ 0 \\ -3 \end{bmatrix} \text{ then } x = 1, y = 0 \text{ and } z = -3.$$

8.2. Operational rules for matrices. A matrix is a new symbol for an ordered set of elements as in the case of representation of a point by its coordinates, and one of wide applications. We can define operations on matrices in any way we find convenient. The most important properties of matrices are given below as the rules of operation.

Rule 1 : (Multiplication by a constant).

If A is a matrix and c is a number, then cA is the matrix obtained by multiplying each element of A by the number c.

For example, let $c=5$ and A be $\begin{bmatrix} 2 & 3 & 5 \\ 1 & 2 & 0 \end{bmatrix}$.

Then $cA=5A=\begin{bmatrix} 10 & 15 & 25 \\ 5 & 10 & 0 \end{bmatrix}$.

Rule 2: (Addition of matrices.)

If A and B are of the same size and have elements a_{ij} and b_{ij} respectively, we define their sum $A+B$ as the matrix C with the elements C_{ij} such that

$$c_{ij} = a_{ij} + b_{ij}.$$

In other words, the elements of C are the sums of the corresponding elements of A and B. For instance,

If $A = \begin{bmatrix} 5 & 2 & 9 \\ 0 & 1 & 5 \end{bmatrix}$ and $B = \begin{bmatrix} 4 & 3 & 0 \\ 0 & 2 & -2 \end{bmatrix}$, then

$$C=A+B = \begin{bmatrix} 5+4 & 2+3 & 9+0 \\ 0+0 & 1+2 & 5-2 \end{bmatrix}$$

$$= \begin{bmatrix} 9 & 5 & 9 \\ 0 & 3 & 3 \end{bmatrix}.$$

In matrix algebra, subtraction is defined for two matrices of the same size in terms of addition, as in other algebras. We define $A-B=A+(-1)B$.

For example if $A = \begin{bmatrix} 2 & 9 & 6 & 1 \\ 4 & 1 & 3 & -7 \end{bmatrix}$ and $B \begin{bmatrix} 1 & 5 & -3 & 2 \\ 3 & -2 & 4 & -9 \end{bmatrix}$,

we have $-B=(-1)B = \begin{bmatrix} -1 & -5 & 3 & -2 \\ -3 & 2 & -4 & 9 \end{bmatrix}$.

$\therefore A-B=A+(-1)B = \begin{bmatrix} 2-1 & 9-5 & 6+3 & 1-2 \\ 4-3 & 1+2 & 3-4 & -7+9 \end{bmatrix}$

$$= \begin{bmatrix} 1 & 4 & 9 & -1 \\ 1 & 3 & -1 & 2 \end{bmatrix}.$$

Rule 3: (Multiplication of matrices).

If A is an $m \times p$ matrix and B is a $p \times n$ matrix, then the product AB is an $m \times n$ matrix with elements given by

$$c_{ij} = \sum_{k=1}^{p} a_{ik} b_{kj}, \qquad i = 1, 2, \ldots\ldots m \text{ and}$$

$$j = 1, 2, \ldots\ldots n.$$

Let $A = \begin{bmatrix} a_{11} & a_{12} \\ a_{21} & a_{22} \end{bmatrix}$ and $B = \begin{bmatrix} b_{11} & b_{12} \\ b_{21} & b_{22} \end{bmatrix}$ be 2×2 matrices.

Then $C = A \cdot B = \begin{bmatrix} c_{11} & c_{12} \\ c_{21} & c_{22} \end{bmatrix}$ where,

$c_{11} = a_{11} b_{11} + a_{12} b_{21}$, $c_{12} = a_{11} b_{12} + a_{12} b_{22}$,

$c_{21} = a_{21} b_{11} + a_{22} b_{21}$, $c_{22} = a_{21} b_{12} + a_{22} b_{22}$.

The rule will be clearer if we take a simple example.

If $A = \begin{bmatrix} 2 & 3 \\ 3 & -4 \\ -5 & 6 \end{bmatrix}$ and $B = \begin{bmatrix} a & b \\ c & d \end{bmatrix}$ A is a 3×2, matrix and B is a 2×2 matrix.

$$C = A \cdot B = \begin{bmatrix} 2a+3c & 2b+3d \\ 3a-4c & 3b-4d \\ -5a+6c & -5b+6d \end{bmatrix}.$$

Here the element c_{11} in the first row and first column of C is obtained by multiplying the elements of the first row of A respectively by the corresponding elements of the first column of B and then adding the results. This is $2a+3c$. The element in the first row and second column of C, c_{12}, is found by multiplying the elements of the *first row* of A respectively by the corresponding elements of the second column of B and then adding the results. This is $2b+3d$.

Now the element in the second row and the first column of C, c_{21} is obtained by multiplying the elements of the second row of A respectively by corresponding elements of the first column of B and then adding the results. That is $3a-4c$. The element in the second row and the second column i.e. c_{22} is obtained by multiplying the elements of the second row of A respectively by the corresponding elements of the second column of B. That is $3b-4d$ and so on. In general, the element c_{ik} is found by multiplying ith row and kth column i.e. multiplying corresponding elements of ith row and kth column and adding them up.

The rule will be clear from the following examples, which should be carefully studied. It is important to note that the product of the matrices is *defined* only when the number of columns in the first matrix is equal to the number of rows in the second matrix. The two matrices must be of the types $m \times p$ and $p \times n$. In other cases, the product is not defined. Thus products of 1×2 and 2×2 or 2×3 matrices is possible and not of 2×3 and 2×2.

Example 1: $\begin{bmatrix} 1 & 2 \end{bmatrix} \cdot \begin{bmatrix} x \\ y \end{bmatrix} = \begin{bmatrix} 1 \cdot x + 2 \cdot y \end{bmatrix} = \begin{bmatrix} x + 2y \end{bmatrix}.$

The product of 1×2 matrix and 2×1 matrix is 1×1 matrix $[x+2y]$ i.e. 1×1 matrix with a single element.

Example 2: $\begin{bmatrix} a & b \\ c & d \end{bmatrix} \cdot \begin{bmatrix} p & q \\ r & s \end{bmatrix} = \begin{bmatrix} ap + br & aq + bs \\ cp + dr & cq + ds \end{bmatrix}.$

Here the product of a 2×2 matrix with another 2×2 matrix gives a 2×2 matrix. Note how to find the elements of each row in the product matrix.

Example 3: Find $A \cdot B$ where $A = \begin{bmatrix} -1 & 2 & -1 \\ -2 & 1 & 3 \end{bmatrix}$

and $B = \begin{bmatrix} 2 & -1 & 1 \\ 1 & 3 & -2 \\ -1 & 2 & 1 \end{bmatrix}$. The first row of $A \cdot B$, is $\begin{bmatrix} -1 & 2 & -1 \end{bmatrix} \times \begin{bmatrix} 2 & -1 & 1 \\ 1 & 3 & -2 \\ -1 & 2 & 1 \end{bmatrix}$

$= [-1\cdot2+2\cdot1+(-1) \quad (-1)+(-1)(-1)+2\cdot3+(-1\cdot2)$

$(-1)1+2\cdot(-2)-1\cdot1]$

$= \begin{bmatrix} 1 & 5 & -6 \end{bmatrix}$

The second row of $A \cdot B$ is

$\begin{bmatrix} -2 & 1 & 3 \end{bmatrix} \times \begin{bmatrix} 2 & -1 & 1 \\ 1 & 3 & -2 \\ -1 & 2 & 1 \end{bmatrix}$

$= [(-2) (2) \quad +1\cdot1 +3(-1) \quad -2(-1)+1\cdot3+3\cdot2$

$\qquad -2\cdot1 +1(-2)+3\cdot1]$

$= \begin{bmatrix} -6 & 11 & -1 \end{bmatrix}$

$AB = \begin{bmatrix} 1 & 5 & -6 \\ -6 & 11 & -1 \end{bmatrix}$

A is 2×3 matrix, B is 3×3 matrix and $AB = 2 \times 3$ matrix.

Example 4: Find AB if $A = \begin{bmatrix} 2 & -1 & 3 \\ 1 & -2 & -1 \end{bmatrix}$ and $B = \begin{bmatrix} 3 & -1 \\ 1 & 2 \\ -1 & 1 \end{bmatrix}$.

Here A is a 2×3 matrix and B is a 3×2 matrix.

∴ the product can be found and is a 2×2 matrix.

The first row in AB is $2 \times 3 - 1 \times 1 + 3 \times (-1)$,

$2 \times (-1) - 1 \times 2 + 3 \times 1$ or $[2, -1]$, the elements of the first row of A multiplied respectively by those of the first and second columns of B added up.

The second row in AB is $[1 \times 3 - 2 \times 1 - 1 \times (-1), \ 1 \times (-1) +$

$(-2) (2) + (-1) (1)]$ or $[2 \quad -6]$.

These are the elements of the second row of A multiplied respectively by those of the first and second columns of B added up. $\therefore A \cdot B = \begin{bmatrix} 2 & -1 \\ 2 & -6 \end{bmatrix}$

According to our rule of multiplication, AB is not identical with BA except in very special cases.   In some cases AB may be defined but BA may not be defined.   For instance, if A is 2×3 matrix and B is 3×4 matrix, $A \cdot B$ is defined but not $B \cdot A$.

Example 5: Find AB and BA if $A = \begin{bmatrix} 1 & -1 \\ 2 & 3 \end{bmatrix}$ and $B = \begin{bmatrix} 3 & 4 \\ 2 & 7 \end{bmatrix}$

$$AB = \begin{bmatrix} 1 & -1 \\ 2 & 3 \end{bmatrix} \cdot \begin{bmatrix} 3 & 4 \\ 2 & 7 \end{bmatrix}$$

$$= \begin{bmatrix} 1 \times 3 - 1 \times 2 & 1 \times 4 - 1 \times 7 \\ 2 \times 3 + 3 \times 2 & 2 \times 4 + 3 \times 7 \end{bmatrix}$$

$$= \begin{bmatrix} 1 & -3 \\ 12 & 29 \end{bmatrix}$$

$$BA = \begin{bmatrix} 3 & 4 \\ 2 & 7 \end{bmatrix} \cdot \begin{bmatrix} 1 & -1 \\ 2 & 3 \end{bmatrix}$$

$$= \begin{bmatrix} 3 \times 1 + 4 \times 2 & 3 \times (-1) + 4 \times 3 \\ 2 \times 1 + 7 \times 2 & 2 \times (-1) + 7 \times 3 \end{bmatrix}$$

$$= \begin{bmatrix} 11 & 9 \\ 16 & 19 \end{bmatrix}$$

$\therefore A \cdot B$ is not the same as $B \cdot A$.

Example 6: Find x, y if

$$\begin{bmatrix} x \\ y \end{bmatrix} = \begin{bmatrix} 2 & 1 \\ 3 & -1 \end{bmatrix} \cdot \begin{bmatrix} 1 \\ 3 \end{bmatrix}$$

$$= \begin{bmatrix} 2+3 \\ 3-3 \end{bmatrix}$$

$$= \begin{bmatrix} 5 \\ 0 \end{bmatrix}$$

$\therefore x = 5, \ y = 0.$

Example 7:   If $A = \begin{bmatrix} 1 & 0 \\ 0 & 1 \end{bmatrix}$ and $B = \begin{bmatrix} 2 & 3 \\ 3 & 4 \end{bmatrix}$

find $A \cdot B$.

$$\begin{bmatrix} 1 & 0 \\ 0 & 1 \end{bmatrix} \cdot \begin{bmatrix} 2 & 3 \\ 3 & 4 \end{bmatrix} = \begin{bmatrix} 1\cdot2+0\cdot3 & 1\cdot3+0\cdot4 \\ 0\cdot2+1\cdot3 & 0\cdot3+1\cdot4 \end{bmatrix}$$

$$= \begin{bmatrix} 2 & 3 \\ 3 & 4 \end{bmatrix} = B.$$

Here $A \cdot B = B$. This is due to the fact that A is a unit matrix. Since the product of a unit matrix with another matrix of the same order is the latter matrix, the unit matrix is also called the *identity matrix*. In such cases $A \cdot B = B \cdot A = B$.

For, $\begin{bmatrix} 2 & 3 \\ 3 & 4 \end{bmatrix} \cdot \begin{bmatrix} 1 & 0 \\ 0 & 1 \end{bmatrix} = \begin{bmatrix} 2+0 & 0+3 \\ 3+0 & 0+4 \end{bmatrix} = \begin{bmatrix} 2 & 3 \\ 3 & 4 \end{bmatrix} = B$

If I stands for a unit matrix $\begin{bmatrix} 1 & 0 \\ 0 & 1 \end{bmatrix}$,

$$I^2 = I \cdot I = \begin{bmatrix} 1 & 0 \\ 0 & 1 \end{bmatrix} \cdot \begin{bmatrix} 1 & 0 \\ 0 & 1 \end{bmatrix} = \begin{bmatrix} 1+0 & 0+0 \\ 0+0 & 0+1 \end{bmatrix}$$

$$= \begin{bmatrix} 1 & 0 \\ 0 & 1 \end{bmatrix} = I.$$ If we multiply I^2 by I, the product is still I.

$\therefore I = I^2 = I^3 = \ldots\ldots = I^n$ where n is any positive integer. Every I is a square matrix i.e. is a 2×2 matrix, 3×3 matrix, $\ldots\ldots$ or $n \times n$ matrix. For instance, $\begin{vmatrix} 1 & 0 \\ 0 & 1 \end{vmatrix}$ is of order 2 and is denoted by I_2 and $\begin{vmatrix} 1 & 0 & 0 \\ 0 & 1 & 0 \\ 0 & 0 & 1 \end{vmatrix}$ is of order 3 and is denoted by I_3 and so on.

Example 8: If $A = \begin{bmatrix} -1 & 1 & 1 \\ 1 & -1 & 1 \\ 1 & 1 & -1 \end{bmatrix}$ and $B = \begin{bmatrix} 0 & \frac{1}{2} & \frac{1}{2} \\ \frac{1}{2} & 0 & \frac{1}{2} \\ \frac{1}{2} & \frac{1}{2} & 0 \end{bmatrix}$

find the product $A \cdot B$.

$$A \cdot B = \begin{bmatrix} 0+\frac{1}{2}+\frac{1}{2} & -\frac{1}{2}+0+\frac{1}{2} & -\frac{1}{2}+\frac{1}{2}+0 \\ 0-\frac{1}{2}+\frac{1}{2} & \frac{1}{2}+0+\frac{1}{2} & \frac{1}{2}-\frac{1}{2}+0 \\ 0+\frac{1}{2}-\frac{1}{2} & \frac{1}{2}+0-\frac{1}{2} & \frac{1}{2}+\frac{1}{2}+0 \end{bmatrix}$$

$$= \begin{bmatrix} 1 & 0 & 0 \\ 0 & 1 & 0 \\ 0 & 0 & 1 \end{bmatrix} \text{ This is } I \text{ of order } 3 \times 3.$$

Exercise 8.1

1. Find the sum of the matrices $\begin{bmatrix} 4 & 5 \\ -3 & 7 \end{bmatrix}$ and $\begin{bmatrix} -2 & 6 \\ 4 & -5 \end{bmatrix}$

2. Solve the following matrix equation for A

$$A = \begin{bmatrix} 3 & 2 & -1 \\ 4 & 6 & 0 \end{bmatrix} + \begin{bmatrix} -2 & 1 & 5 \\ 0 & 4 & -2 \end{bmatrix}$$

3. $A - \begin{bmatrix} 3 & 5 \\ 2 & 7 \end{bmatrix} = \begin{bmatrix} 1 & 2 \\ 0 & 3 \end{bmatrix}$

4. $2A - 3 \begin{bmatrix} 2 & -1 & 3 \\ -3 & 0 & 1 \end{bmatrix} = \begin{bmatrix} 3 & 1 & 2 \\ 1 & 2 & 3 \end{bmatrix}$

5. $A = 2 \begin{bmatrix} 2 & 3 \\ -5 & 1 \end{bmatrix} - 3 \begin{bmatrix} 7 & 10 \\ -3 & -11 \end{bmatrix}$

6. $2A = 3 \begin{bmatrix} 2 & -3 & 4 \\ 0 & 2 & -2 \end{bmatrix} - 2 \begin{bmatrix} 1 & -3 & 5 \\ 2 & 3 & -1 \end{bmatrix}$

7. $2A - 3 \begin{bmatrix} 3 & 0 & 5 \\ 2 & 1 & 4 \end{bmatrix} = \begin{bmatrix} 1 & 2 & 3 \\ 3 & -1 & 2 \end{bmatrix}$

8. $3A + \begin{bmatrix} 1 & 2 \\ 3 & 5 \end{bmatrix} = 2 \begin{bmatrix} 2 & 7 \\ 3 & 4 \end{bmatrix}$

Solve simultaneously for A and B

9. $A - 2B = \begin{bmatrix} 2 & 3 \\ -1 & 1 \end{bmatrix}, \quad A - B = \begin{bmatrix} 3 & 2 \\ 1 & -1 \end{bmatrix}.$

10. $A - B = \begin{bmatrix} 3 & 5 \\ 1 & 2 \end{bmatrix}, \quad A + B = \begin{bmatrix} 1 & 1 \\ 3 & 2 \end{bmatrix}.$

11. $A+2B = \begin{bmatrix} 2 & 1 & 0 \\ 1 & -1 & 2 \end{bmatrix}, \quad 2A+3B = \begin{bmatrix} 1 & 2 & -1 \\ 2 & 0 & 1 \end{bmatrix}.$

12. $2A-B = \begin{bmatrix} 3 & -3 & 0 \\ 3 & 3 & 2 \end{bmatrix},$

$\qquad 2B+A = \begin{bmatrix} 4 & 1 & 5 \\ -1 & 4 & -4 \end{bmatrix}.$

Work out the products AB and BA:

13. $A = \begin{bmatrix} 3 & 2 \\ 2 & 3 \end{bmatrix}$ and $B = \begin{bmatrix} 1 & 1 \\ 2 & 3 \end{bmatrix}.$

14. $A = \begin{bmatrix} 2 & -2 \\ 4 & 6 \end{bmatrix}$ and $B = \begin{bmatrix} 3 & -1 \\ 2 & 3 \end{bmatrix}.$

15. $A = \begin{bmatrix} 3 & 2 \\ 5 & -2 \end{bmatrix}$ and $B = \begin{bmatrix} 2 & 3 \\ 4 & 5 \end{bmatrix}.$

16. $A = \begin{bmatrix} 2 & 6 \\ 4 & 8 \end{bmatrix}$ and $B = \begin{bmatrix} 3 & 6 \\ 9 & -12 \end{bmatrix}.$

17. $A = \begin{bmatrix} 15 & 11 \\ -7 & 9 \end{bmatrix}$ and $B = \begin{bmatrix} 3 & 2 \\ -5 & -2 \end{bmatrix}.$

18. $A = \begin{bmatrix} 1 & 0 & 2 \\ -2 & 1 & 3 \end{bmatrix}$ and $B = \begin{bmatrix} 4 & 2 \\ -2 & 2 \\ 2 & 4 \end{bmatrix}.$

19. $A = \begin{bmatrix} 1 & 2 & -1 \\ -2 & 1 & 3 \end{bmatrix}$ and $B = \begin{bmatrix} 3 & 1 & 5 \\ 1 & 2 & -2 \\ -1 & -2 & 3 \end{bmatrix}.$

20. $A = \begin{bmatrix} 1 & 0 & 0 \\ 0 & 1 & 0 \\ 0 & 0 & 1 \end{bmatrix}$ and $B = \begin{bmatrix} 1 & 2 & 3 \\ 2 & 3 & 4 \\ 3 & 4 & 5 \end{bmatrix}.$

21. $A = \begin{bmatrix} 1 & 0 & 0 \\ 0 & 1 & 0 \\ 0 & 0 & 1 \end{bmatrix}$ and $B = \begin{bmatrix} 2 & 0 & 0 \\ 0 & 2 & 0 \\ 0 & 0 & 2 \end{bmatrix}.$

22. $A = \begin{bmatrix} 1 & 1 & 0 \\ 0 & 0 & 0 \\ 0 & 1 & 0 \end{bmatrix}$ and $B = \begin{bmatrix} 0 & 0 & 0 \\ 0 & 0 & 0 \\ 1 & 0 & 0 \end{bmatrix}.$

23. Show that $\begin{bmatrix} 1 & -1 \\ 1 & 0 \\ 0 & 1 \end{bmatrix} \cdot \begin{bmatrix} 0 \\ 1 \end{bmatrix} = \begin{bmatrix} -1 \\ 0 \\ 1 \end{bmatrix}$.

24. Form the product $\begin{bmatrix} 1 & 5 & -1 \\ 2 & 4 & -2 \\ 3 & 2 & 6 \end{bmatrix} \cdot \begin{bmatrix} 0 & 1 & 0 \\ 1 & 0 & 0 \\ 0 & 0 & 1 \end{bmatrix}$.

Find the values of the unknowns in the following equations:

25. $\begin{bmatrix} x \\ y \end{bmatrix} = \begin{bmatrix} 1 & 2 \\ 3 & 4 \end{bmatrix} \cdot \begin{bmatrix} 0 \\ 1 \end{bmatrix}$

26. $\begin{bmatrix} x \\ y \end{bmatrix} = \begin{bmatrix} 1 & 2 & 3 \\ 4 & 5 & 6 \end{bmatrix} \cdot \begin{bmatrix} 1 \\ 0 \\ 2 \end{bmatrix}$

27. $\begin{bmatrix} 1 & 0 \\ 0 & 1 \end{bmatrix} \cdot \begin{bmatrix} x \\ y \end{bmatrix} = \begin{bmatrix} 1 & 0 \\ 2 & -1 \end{bmatrix} \cdot \begin{bmatrix} 3 \\ 2 \end{bmatrix}$

28. $\begin{bmatrix} x \\ y \\ z \end{bmatrix} = \begin{bmatrix} -1 & 0 & 1 \\ 2 & 1 & 0 \\ 1 & 2 & 3 \end{bmatrix} \cdot \begin{bmatrix} 1 \\ 2 \\ 3 \end{bmatrix}$

29. $\begin{bmatrix} x \\ y \\ z \end{bmatrix} = \begin{bmatrix} 1 & 2 & 3 \\ 0 & 1 & -1 \\ 2 & 1 & 0 \end{bmatrix} \cdot \begin{bmatrix} 2 & 0 \\ 1 & 1 \\ 2 & 3 \end{bmatrix}$

30. $\begin{bmatrix} 1 & 0 & 0 \\ 0 & 1 & 0 \\ 0 & 0 & 1 \end{bmatrix} \cdot \begin{bmatrix} x \\ y \\ z \end{bmatrix} = \begin{bmatrix} 3 \\ 4 \\ 5 \end{bmatrix} \cdot \begin{bmatrix} 1 & -2 & 3 & 0 \end{bmatrix}$

31. Form the product of $\begin{bmatrix} 1 & 1 & 0 \\ 4 & 0 & 2 \\ 2 & 6 & 1 \end{bmatrix} \cdot \begin{bmatrix} 3 & 0 & 2 \\ 2 & 5 & 0 \\ 7 & 2 & 1 \end{bmatrix}$

32. Find the product $\begin{bmatrix} x, & y, & z \end{bmatrix} \cdot \begin{bmatrix} a & h & g \\ h & b & f \\ g & f & c \end{bmatrix} \cdot \begin{bmatrix} x \\ y \\ z \end{bmatrix}$.

8.3. Determinants.

A square matrix with n rows and n columns is said to be of order n. A *submatrix* of a given matrix is any matrix obtained by removing certain rows and columns from the original matrix. Thus a square matrix of order 4

$$\begin{bmatrix} 1 & 2 & 3 & 4 \\ 5 & 6 & 7 & 8 \\ a & b & c & d \\ e & f & g & h \end{bmatrix}$$ has the following submatrices:

[1], [2] etc. with a single element. Here 3 rows and 3 columns are removed.

$$\begin{bmatrix} 1 & 2 \\ 5 & 6 \end{bmatrix}, \begin{bmatrix} a & d \\ e & h \end{bmatrix}$$ etc. are submatrices of order 2,

obtained by removing 2 rows and 2 columns.

$$\begin{bmatrix} 1 & 2 & 3 \\ 5 & 6 & 7 \\ a & b & c \end{bmatrix}, \begin{bmatrix} 2 & 3 & 4 \\ 6 & 7 & 8 \\ f & g & h \end{bmatrix}$$ etc. are submatrices.

of order 3 obtained by removing one row and one column.

Definition: With each square matrix, we associate a real number called the determinant (D) of the matrix. If A is the square matrix, we write the determinant associated with it as Det. A.

A determinant is a function the domain of which is the collection of square matrices; its range is the real number system. If A is a matrix written out as a square array in brackets like this [ ], its determinant is denoted by the same array between two vertical bars.

Thus if $A = \begin{bmatrix} 3 & -1 & 2 \\ 1 & 0 & 5 \\ 7 & -2 & -3 \end{bmatrix}$, then

$A| = \text{Det. } A = \begin{vmatrix} 3 & -1 & 2 \\ 1 & 0 & 5 \\ 7 & -2 & -3 \end{vmatrix}$.

While A stands simply for an array, Det. A has a definite value.

This definition of Determinant associated with a square matrix is built up on the principle of mathematical induction. It is first specified for $n=1$ as Det. $[a_{11}]$ as a_{11}. Then a rule is laid down to express determinants of order n in terms of those of order $n-1$.

$$\textit{Rule}: \text{Det. } A = \begin{vmatrix} a_{11} & a_{12}\ldots\ldots a_{ij}\ldots\ldots a_{in} \\ a_{21} & a_{22}\ldots\ldots a_{2j}\ldots\ldots a_{2n} \\ \cdots\cdots\cdots\cdots\cdots\cdots\cdots \\ a_{i1} & a_{i2}\ldots\ldots a_{ij}\ldots\ldots a_{in} \\ \cdots\cdots\cdots\cdots\cdots\cdots\cdots \\ a_{n1} & a_{n2}\ldots\ldots a_{nj}\ldots\ldots a_{nn} \end{vmatrix} = \sum_{i=1}^{n} (-1)^{i+n} a_{in} A_{in},$$

where A_{in} is the determinant of the $(n-1) \times (n-1)$ submatrix of A, obtained by deleting its ith row and n^{th} column. The determinant A_{in} is called the *minor* of a_{in}.

If $n=2$, Det. $A = \sum_{i=1}^{2} (-1)^{i+2} a_{i2} A_{i2}$

$$= -a_{12} A_{12} + a_{22} A_{22} = -a_{12} a_{21} + a_{22} a_{11}.$$

For, $A_{12}=a_{21}$ and $A_{22}=a_{11}$, as by deleting the row and column containing a_{12} we have a submatrix $[a_{21}]$ and the det. of this submatrix is just a_{21}. Similarly A_{22} is a_{11}

$$\therefore \quad \begin{vmatrix} a_{11} & a_{12} \\ a_{21} & a_{22} \end{vmatrix} = a_{11} a_{22} - a_{12} a_{21}.$$

If $n=3$, $\begin{vmatrix} a_{11} & a_{12} & a_{13} \\ a_{21} & a_{22} & a_{23} \\ a_{31} & a_{32} & a_{33} \end{vmatrix} = \sum_{i=1}^{3} (-1)^{i+3} a_{i3} A_{i3}$

$= a_{13} A_{13} - a_{23} A_{23} + a_{33} A_{33}$ according to the third column

where $A_{13} = \begin{vmatrix} a_{21} & a_{22} \\ a_{31} & a_{32} \end{vmatrix}$, $A_{23} = \begin{vmatrix} a_{11} & a_{12} \\ a_{31} & a_{32} \end{vmatrix}$,

and $A_{33} = \begin{vmatrix} a_{11} & a_{12} \\ a_{21} & a_{22} \end{vmatrix}$.

$$\therefore D = a_{13} (a_{21} a_{32} - a_{22} a_{31}) - a_{23} (a_{11} a_{32} - a_{12} a_{31})$$
$$+ a_{33} (a_{11} a_{22} - a_{12} a_{21}) \quad \ldots \ldots (1)$$
$$= a_{11} (a_{22} a_{33} - a_{23} a_{32}) - a_{21} (a_{12} a_{33} - a_{13} a_{32})$$
$$+ a_{31} (a_{12} a_{23} - a_{13} a_{22}) \quad \ldots \ldots (2) \text{ according}$$
to the first column.
$$= a_{11} (a_{22} a_{33} - a_{23} a_{32}) - a_{12} (a_{21} a_{33} - a_{23} a_{31})$$
$$+ a_{13} (a_{21} a_{32} - a_{22} a_{31}) \quad \ldots \ldots (3) \text{ according}$$
to the first row.

The three forms of expressing the value of D viz. (1), (2) and (3) lead to the same result. It is, therefore, clear that we may start off with any column, with any row. The determinant is, therefore, the algebraic sum of the products obtained by multiplying each element of column or row by its minor. The sign of each such product is $(-1)^{i+j}$ where the element is in the ith row and j^{th} column.

Thus in the above example $(-1)^{1+1} a_{11}$ has the positive sign, $(-1)^{2+1} a_{21}$ or $(-1)^{1+2} a_{12}$ has negative sign and so on.

Minors and cofactors.

A minor of an element a_{ij} in the square matrix of order $n (\geqslant 2)$ is the determinant of the matrix remaining after removing the row and the column containing the element a_{ij}. The cofactor of an element of a matrix is the product of the minor of the element and $(-1)^{i+j}$, where i is the row subscript and j is the column subscript of the element a_{ij}. Thus the determinant of a matrix of the fourth order can be expanded according to the first row as under:

$$D = \begin{vmatrix} a_{11} & a_{12} & a_{13} & a_{14} \\ a_{21} & a_{22} & a_{23} & a_{24} \\ a_{31} & a_{32} & a_{33} & a_{34} \\ a_{41} & a_{42} & a_{43} & a_{44} \end{vmatrix} = \begin{matrix} (-1)^{1+1} a_{11} M_{11} + (-1)^{1+2} a_{12} M_{12} \\ + (-1)^{1+3} a_{13} M_{13} \\ + (-1)^{1+4} a_{14} M_{14} \end{matrix}$$

or $a_{11} C_{11} + a_{12} C_{12} + a_{13} C_{13} + a_{14} C_{14}$

$$= a_{11} M_{11} - a_{12} M_{12} + a_{13} M_{13} - a_{14} M_{14}$$

as $c_{11}=M_{11}$, $c_{12}=-M_{12}$, $C_{13}=-M_{13}$, $C_{14}=-M_{14}$.
Similarly D could be also expanded according to the first column as $a_{11}\,M_{11}-a_{21}\,M_{21}+a_{31}\,M_{31}-a_{41}\,M_{41}$.
Here M_{11} is the minor of a_{11} and stands for

$$\begin{vmatrix} a_{22} & a_{23} & a_{24} \\ a_{32} & a_{33} & a_{34} \\ a_{42} & a_{43} & a_{44} \end{vmatrix}$$ and the sign of $a_{11}\,M_{11}$ is $(-1)^{1+1}$ or

positive; M_{21} is the minor of a_{21} and stands for

$$\begin{vmatrix} a_{12} & a_{13} & a_{14} \\ a_{32} & a_{33} & a_{34} \\ a_{42} & a_{43} & a_{44} \end{vmatrix}$$ and the sign of $a_{21}\,M_{21}$ is $(-1)^{2+1}$ or—

and so on. This is the expansion of the determinant according to the first column.
If we develop the determinant according to the second column,

$$D = -a_{12}\begin{vmatrix} a_{21} & a_{23} & a_{24} \\ a_{31} & a_{33} & a_{34} \\ a_{41} & a_{43} & a_{44} \end{vmatrix} + a_{22}\begin{vmatrix} a_{11} & a_{13} & a_{14} \\ a_{31} & a_{33} & a_{34} \\ a_{41} & a_{43} & a_{44} \end{vmatrix}$$

$$-a_{32}\begin{vmatrix} a_{11} & a_{13} & a_{14} \\ a_{21} & a_{23} & a_{24} \\ a_{41} & a_{43} & a_{44} \end{vmatrix} + a_{42}\begin{vmatrix} a_{11} & a_{13} & a_{14} \\ a_{21} & a_{23} & a_{24} \\ a_{31} & a_{33} & a_{34} \end{vmatrix}$$

Here $(-1)^{2+2}$ and $(-1)^{4+2}$ are positive and
$(-1)^{1+2}$ and $(-1)^{3+2}$ are negative.
We are now in a position to evaluate any determinant.

7.4. The actual evaluation of a determinant of high order by expansion on the lines suggested above is somewhat tedious. The following rules are useful in such evaluation.

Rule 1 : If the corresponding rows and columns of a matrix are interchanged, its determinant remains unchanged.

Consider for example $$\begin{vmatrix} a_{11} & a_{12} & a_{13} \\ a_{21} & a_{22} & a_{23} \\ a_{31} & a_{32} & a_{33} \end{vmatrix} \text{ and } \begin{vmatrix} a_{11} & a_{21} & a_{31} \\ a_{12} & a_{22} & a_{32} \\ a_{13} & a_{23} & a_{33} \end{vmatrix}$$

Here the first row has been changed into the first column, the second row into the second column and so on.

The first determinant

$$= a_{13} (a_{21} a_{32} - a_{22} a_{31}) - a_{23} (a_{11} a_{32} - a_{12} a_{31})$$
$$+ a_{33} (a_{11} a_{22} - a_{12} a_{21})$$

and the second determinant

$$= a_{31} (a_{12} a_{23} - a_{22} a_{13}) - a_{32} (a_{11} a_{23} - a_{21} a_{13})$$
$$+ a_{33} (a_{11} a_{22} - a_{21} a_{12})$$ according to the third

column in both cases.

We see that the cofactors of any element of the first is the same as the cofactor of the same element in the second determinant.   ∴ the two determinants have the same value.

The result is true whatever be the order of the corresponding matrix.   We need not attempt to prove it at this stage.

Rule 2 : If all the elements in the kth row or kth column $(1 \leqslant k \leqslant n)$ of a matrix A are zeros, then Det. $A = 0$.

Expanding the determinant, some element or the other of the kth row (or kth column) will appear in each term of the expansion.   This means that we introduce the factor zero in each term.   Hence the determinant is zero.

Rule 3 : If a matrix A' is obtained from A by multiplying the elements of the kth row or column by a constant c, then the Det. $A' = c$ Det. A.   Each term of expansion in A is multiplied by c.   Hence the result.

Rule 4 : If each element a_{ij} of the ith row (or jth column) is equal to $b_{ij} + c_{ij}$, then Det. $A =$ Det. $B +$ Det. C, where A, B and C differ only in their ith row (or jth column).

Each term of the expression contains some term or the other ith row (or the jth column).   If we replace the term a_{ij} by $b_{ij} + c_{ij}$, we have the expansion of two determinants with changes only in the ith row.   ∴ Det. $A =$ Det. $B +$ Det. C.

For example,

$$\begin{vmatrix} a_{11} & a_{12} \\ a_{21} & a_{22} \end{vmatrix} = \begin{vmatrix} a_{11} & a_{12} \\ b_{21}+c_{21} & b_{22}+c_{22} \end{vmatrix} = \begin{matrix} a_{11}(b_{22}+c_{22}) \\ -a_{12}(b_{21}+c_{21}) \end{matrix}$$

$$= a_{11}b_{22}-a_{12}b_{21}+a_{11}c_{22}-a_{12}c_{21} = \begin{vmatrix} a_{11} & a_{12} \\ b_{21} & b_{22} \end{vmatrix} +$$

$$\begin{vmatrix} a_{11} & a_{12} \\ c_{21} & c_{22} \end{vmatrix} = \text{Dct. } B + \text{Det. } C.$$

Rule 5: If Det. A' is obtained from Det. A by interchanging two rows or (columns), then Det. $A = -$Det. A'. If $n=1$, there is only one term a_{11}, there is nothing to prove.

If $n=2$, $\begin{vmatrix} a_{11} & a_{12} \\ a_{21} & a_{22} \end{vmatrix} = a_{11}a_{22}-a_{12}a_{21} = - \begin{vmatrix} a_{21} & a_{22} \\ a_{11} & a_{12} \end{vmatrix}.$

If $n=3$, $\begin{vmatrix} a_{11} & a_{12} & a_{13} \\ a_{21} & a_{22} & a_{23} \\ a_{31} & a_{32} & a_{33} \end{vmatrix} = a_{13} \begin{vmatrix} a_{21} & a_{22} \\ a_{31} & a_{32} \end{vmatrix} -a_{23} \begin{vmatrix} a_{11} & a_{12} \\ a_{31} & a_{32} \end{vmatrix}$

$+ a_{33} \begin{vmatrix} a_{11} & a_{12} \\ a_{21} & a_{22} \end{vmatrix} = a_{13}(a_{21}a_{32}-a_{22}a_{31})-a_{23}(a_{11}a_{32}$
$-a_{12}a_{31})+a_{33}(a_{11}a_{22}-a_{12}a_{21})\ldots(1)$

If the second row and the 3rd row interchange,

We have $\begin{vmatrix} a_{11} & a_{12} & a_{13} \\ a_{31} & a_{32} & a_{33} \\ a_{21} & a_{22} & a_{23} \end{vmatrix} = a_{13} \begin{vmatrix} a_{31} & a_{32} \\ a_{21} & a_{22} \end{vmatrix} -a_{33} \begin{vmatrix} a_{11} & a_{12} \\ a_{21} & a_{22} \end{vmatrix}$

$$+ a_{23} \begin{vmatrix} a_{11} & a_{12} \\ a_{31} & a_{32} \end{vmatrix}$$

$$= a_{13}(a_{31}a_{22}-a_{21}a_{32})-a_{33}(a_{11}a_{22}-a_{12}a_{21})$$
$$+ a_{23}(a_{11}a_{32}-a_{12}a_{31}) \ldots (2).$$

There is no difference in the expansion of (1) and of (2) except in the sign throughout. Similarly we can deal with 4th and higher orders.

Corollary 1: If the elements of two rows (or of columns) of a determinant D are proportional, then determinant D is zero.

If the elements of one row (or column) of D are c times those of another row (or column), $D = c\,D'$ by Rule 3 where D' has two identical rows or columns. Interchanging these rows or columns of D', D' remains unchanged except in the sign and by Rule 5 above, $D' = -D'$. $\therefore D' = 0$ and $D = c \cdot D' = 0$.

Rule 6 : If each element of any row (or column) of a matrix is multiplied by the same number k and added to the corresponding element of another row (or column), then the associated determinants are the same.

Take for example a matrix of 4th order. The determinant may be expressed in the form

$$
D = \begin{vmatrix}
a_{11} & a_{12} & a_{13} & a_{14} \\
a_{21} & a_{22} & a_{23} & a_{24} \\
a_{31} & a_{32} & a_{33} & a_{34} \\
a_{41} & a_{42} & a_{43} & a_{44}
\end{vmatrix}.
$$

Now suppose the second row is multiplied by k and added to the first row, we have by Rule 4

$$
\begin{vmatrix}
a_{11}+k\,a_{21} & a_{12}+k\,a_{22} & a_{13}+k\,a_{23} & a_{14}+ka_{24} \\
a_{21} & a_{22} & a_{23} & a_{24} \\
a_{31} & a_{32} & a_{33} & a_{34} \\
a_{41} & a_{42} & a_{43} & a_{44}
\end{vmatrix}
$$

$$
= \begin{vmatrix}
a_{11} & a_{12} & a_{13} & a_{14} \\
a_{21} & a_{22} & a_{23} & a_{24} \\
a_{31} & a_{32} & a_{33} & a_{34} \\
a_{41} & a_{42} & a_{43} & a_{44}
\end{vmatrix}
+ k \begin{vmatrix}
a_{21} & a_{22} & a_{23} & a_{24} \\
a_{21} & a_{22} & a_{23} & a_{24} \\
a_{31} & a_{32} & a_{33} & a_{34} \\
a_{41} & a_{42} & a_{43} & a_{44}
\end{vmatrix}
$$

$= D + 0$ by Rule 5
$= D$

In evaluating the determinant we can now take any column (or row) to start with and not necessarily the last or the first one, as the chosen column or row can be transferred to the last or the first column (or row), with the appropriate sign according to Rule 5. We can simplify the work by using Rule 6 and introducing as many zeros as possible.

Example 1 : Find the value of the determinant

$$\begin{vmatrix} 3 & -1 & 2 & 6 \\ 2 & 3 & 5 & 4 \\ 4 & -2 & 2 & 7 \\ -3 & 2 & -1 & 3 \end{vmatrix}$$

We see that by adding the elements of the second column to the corresponding ones of the first column,

we have
$$\begin{vmatrix} 3-1 & -1 & 2 & 6 \\ 2+3 & 3 & 5 & 4 \\ 4-2 & -2 & 2 & 7 \\ -3+2 & 2 & -1 & 3 \end{vmatrix} = \begin{vmatrix} 2 & -1 & 2 & 6 \\ 5 & 3 & 5 & 4 \\ 2 & -2 & 2 & 7 \\ -1 & 2 & -1 & 3 \end{vmatrix}$$

We notice that the elements of the first column are equal to those of the 3rd column.

∴ the determinant is zero.

Example 2 : Evaluate
$$\begin{vmatrix} 4 & 1 & -3 & 0 \\ -6 & 0 & -3 & 4 \\ 2 & -1 & 3 & -2 \\ 4 & 1 & -15 & 2 \end{vmatrix}.$$

Adding the third row to the first and fourth rows in turn we have,

$$D = \begin{vmatrix} 6 & 0 & 0 & -2 \\ -6 & 0 & -3 & 4 \\ 2 & -1 & 3 & -2 \\ 6 & 0 & -12 & 0 \end{vmatrix}$$

The rule of expansion is that if we expand by starting with the first column we begin with the positive sign, if we start with the second column, we begin with negative sign, if we start with the third column, we begin with the positive sign and so on. The same rule holds good in the case of rows.

Let us expand according to the second column as there are 3 zeros. It will start with −1. This negative sign and the negative sign of the second column will make it positive i.e. $(-1)(-1)^{i+j} = -(-1)^{3+2} = 1$.

$$D = \begin{vmatrix} 6 & 0 & -2 \\ -6 & -3 & 4 \\ 6 & -12 & 0 \end{vmatrix} = -6 \times 3 \times 2 \begin{vmatrix} 1 & 0 & -1 \\ -1 & 1 & 2 \\ 1 & 4 & 0 \end{vmatrix}$$

$$\therefore D = -36 \begin{vmatrix} 0 & 1 & 1 \\ -1 & 1 & 2 \\ 0 & 5 & 2 \end{vmatrix} = (-36) \times (-3)$$

$$= 108$$

Here we first take out the common factors of the three columns. Then add the second row to the first and third rows.

Exercise 8.2

Evaluate the following determinants 1 to 5 by expanding according to (a) the 2nd row and (b) the 3rd column

1. $\begin{vmatrix} 2 & 3 & -1 \\ 1 & -2 & 5 \\ 3 & 4 & 2 \end{vmatrix}$ **2.** $\begin{vmatrix} 1 & 7 & 3 \\ -3 & 2 & 4 \\ 1 & 3 & 2 \end{vmatrix}$

3. $\begin{vmatrix} -2 & 1 & 3 \\ 1 & 2 & -2 \\ -2 & 1 & 3 \end{vmatrix}$ **4.** $\begin{vmatrix} 2 & 1 & 0 \\ 3 & -6 & \frac{1}{3} \\ 2 & 1 & 10 \end{vmatrix}$

5. $\begin{vmatrix} a & h & g \\ h & b & f \\ g & f & c \end{vmatrix}$

Evaluate:

6. $\begin{vmatrix} 1 & 1 & 1 & 1 \\ 2 & 0 & -2 & 0 \\ 0 & 3 & 3 & -3 \\ 2 & 0 & -1 & -3 \end{vmatrix}$ **7.** $\begin{vmatrix} 1 & -1 & 3 & 2 \\ 2 & -2 & 2 & -1 \\ 3 & 0 & 0 & -2 \\ 4 & 3 & 1 & 1 \end{vmatrix}$

8. $\begin{vmatrix} 7 & 3 & 0 & -1 \\ -5 & -7 & 0 & -2 \\ 3 & 0 & 0 & -2 \\ 4 & 3 & 1 & 1 \end{vmatrix}$ **9.** $\begin{vmatrix} 4 & -4 & 2 & 6 \\ 0 & 2 & -1 & -1 \\ 2 & -3 & 2 & 4 \\ 0 & -3 & 3 & 3 \end{vmatrix}$

10. $\begin{vmatrix} 3 & -2 & 12 & 4 \\ 1 & 0 & 4 & -1 \\ 5 & 4 & 6 & 0 \\ 2 & 2 & -12 & 6 \end{vmatrix}$ **11.** $\begin{vmatrix} 4 & 2 & 5 & 6 \\ 2 & 1 & 0 & 3 \\ 7 & 2 & -3 & 2 \\ 4 & -1 & 7 & 5 \end{vmatrix}$

Simplify and evaluate:

12. $\begin{vmatrix} 4 & 6 & 12 & 6 \\ 0 & 2 & 6 & 2 \\ -1 & -2 & 0 & 4 \\ 1 & 2 & 0 & 3 \end{vmatrix}$ **13.** $\begin{vmatrix} 3 & 1 & -3 & -1 \\ 2 & 3 & -4 & -1 \\ 5 & -2 & 3 & -6 \\ -2 & -3 & 1 & 4 \end{vmatrix}$

14. $\begin{vmatrix} -2 & 3 & 2 & 4 \\ -3 & 1 & -2 & 3 \\ 2 & 2 & 3 & -2 \\ 4 & -3 & 2 & 1 \end{vmatrix}$ **15.** $\begin{vmatrix} 3 & -2 & 6 & 4 \\ 5 & 4 & 3 & 0 \\ 1 & 0 & 2 & -1 \\ 2 & 2 & -5 & 6 \end{vmatrix}$

16. $\begin{vmatrix} 2 & -1 & 0 & 3 \\ 1 & 2 & -1 & -3 \\ 3 & 0 & 2 & 0 \\ 4 & 3 & 1 & 2 \end{vmatrix}$ **17.** $\begin{vmatrix} 3 & -1 & 2 & 6 \\ 2 & 3 & 5 & 4 \\ 4 & -2 & 2 & 7 \\ -3 & 2 & -1 & -3 \end{vmatrix}$

18. Prove that $\begin{vmatrix} 1 & x & x^2 & x^3 \\ 1 & y & y^2 & y^3 \\ 1 & z & z^2 & z^3 \\ 1 & t & t^2 & t^3 \end{vmatrix}$

$= (x-y)\,(y-z)\,(z-t)\,(x-z)\,(x-t)\,(y-t).$

19. Prove that if $x+y+z=0$, then the determinant

$\begin{vmatrix} 0 & x & -y & -z \\ -x & 0 & xy-z^2 & y^2-zx \\ y & z^2-xy & 0 & x^2-yz \\ z & zx-y^2 & yz-x^2 & 0 \end{vmatrix} = 0$

20. Prove that the determinant $\begin{vmatrix} a & b & c & 0 \\ 0 & a & b & c \\ c & 0 & a & b \\ b & c & 0 & a \end{vmatrix} =$

$(a+b+c)\,(a-b+c)\,(a^2+b^2+c^2-2ac).$

8.4. The Rank of a Matrix.

We have seen that a determinant (D) is associated with each square matrix. A square matrix is said to be *nonsingular* if its determinant is not zero. Otherwise it is singular.

Definition: The rank of an $m \times n$ matrix is the largest integer r for which a nonsingular $r \times r$ submatrix exists. In order to show that a given matrix is of rank r, we have first to show that at least one r-rowed determinant of the matrix is not zero, and secondly that all $(r+1)$-rowed determinants are zero.

For example, consider the matrix $\begin{bmatrix} 3 & 0 & 1 & 0 \\ 2 & 0 & 5 & 0 \\ 1 & 0 & 0 & 0 \end{bmatrix}$ which is a 3×4 matrix. There is no 3×3 matrix the determinant of which is not zero; for any such square submatrix has at least one column entirely consisting of zero elements. Next consider a 2×2 submatrix. For instance $\begin{bmatrix} 3 & 1 \\ 2 & 5 \end{bmatrix}$. The determinant D associated with it $\begin{vmatrix} 3 & 1 \\ 2 & 5 \end{vmatrix}$ is equal to 13. Since this is not zero, the rank of the given matrix is 2. We note that the rank r of any $m \times n$ matrix can never exceed the smaller of the number m and n.

8.5. Elementary transformations.

Definition: By an elementary transformation of a matrix, we mean a transformation of any one of the following ways to obtain a second matrix:

(1) the interchange of two rows or of two columns;
(2) the multiplication of each element of a row (or column) by a non-zero constant,
(3) the addition to the elements of one row (or column) of the products of the corresponding elements of another row (or column) by one and the same constant.

It is clear that if we can pass from one matrix A to another matrix B by one of these transformations, we can pass back from B to A by an elementary transformation. We also note that these transformations are just the same which we used for simplifying and evaluating determinants in the previous section.

Definition 2: Two matrices are said to be *equivalent* if it is possible to pass from one to the other by a finite number of elementary transformations. The fact that A and B are equivalent is written $A \cong B$.

Theorem: If two matrices are equivalent, they have the same rank.

From the method of evaluating determinants, it is clear that the transformations (1) and (2) do not affect the vanishing or non-vanishing of any determinant of the matrix. Hence the rank remains the same in the case of these transformations. It is, therefore, sufficient to prove that the rank of a matrix is not changed by a transformation of the type (3).

Let r be the rank of the matrix A. Suppose we add to the elements of the pth row k times the elements of the qth row, thus giving the equivalent matrix B.

Since A is of rank r, all its $(r+1)$-rowed determinants are zero. Some of these determinants are not changed at all by the transformations, if they do not contain the pth row or if they contain both the pth and the qth row. This is in accordance with the rules of the determinants. We are only concerned with the other determinants viz. those which contain the pth but not the qth row. These determinants take on the form $A' \perp kB'$ where A' and B' are $(r+1)$-rowed determinants of A. But it is given $A' = B' = 0$.

$\therefore$ the transformation (c) does not increase the rank of a matrix.

But the rank of B cannot be less than that of A, for then the transformation (3) which carries B into A would increase the rank of B.

To evaluate the rank of an $m \times n$ matrix directly from the definition may be laborious.   In such cases, this theorem may be used to advantage.

Example 1 : Determine the rank of $\begin{bmatrix} 6 & 14 & 20 & 9 \\ 7 & 6 & 3 & 4 \\ 14 & 12 & 6 & 8 \end{bmatrix}$.

This is 3×4 matrix and the rank cannot be larger than 3. If we take any determinant of 3rd order, for instance,

$\begin{vmatrix} 14 & 20 & 9 \\ 6 & 3 & 4 \\ 12 & 6 & 8 \end{vmatrix}$, we notice the elements of the 3rd row are twice those of the corresponding elements of the second

row.   If we multiply the second row by -2 and add the result to the third row, we have $\begin{vmatrix} 14 & 20 & 9 \\ 6 & 3 & 4 \\ 0 & 0 & 0 \end{vmatrix}$. This is clearly zero.

But the determinants of the second order are not zero.

∴ the rank is 2.

Example 2 : Determine the rank of $\begin{bmatrix} 3 & 2 & -2 \\ 2 & 3 & -3 \\ -2 & 4 & 2 \\ 5 & -2 & 4 \end{bmatrix}$.

This is a matrix of 4 rows and 3 columns and the rank cannot exceed 3.   To check whether all the four determinants of third order are or are not zero, we have to evaluate them. Interchange the first two rows and then multiply the second and fourth by 2.

$$\begin{bmatrix} 3 & 2 & -2 \\ 2 & 3 & -3 \\ -2 & 4 & 2 \\ 5 & -2 & 4 \end{bmatrix} \cong \begin{bmatrix} 2 & 3 & -3 \\ 3 & 2 & -2 \\ -2 & 4 & 2 \\ 5 & -2 & 4 \end{bmatrix} \cong \begin{bmatrix} 2 & 3 & -3 \\ 6 & 4 & -4 \\ -2 & 4 & 2 \\ 10 & -4 & 8 \end{bmatrix}$$

Add the first and third rows, multiply the first row by -3 and add to the second row and multiply the first row by -5 and add to the 4th row, we have now the matrix

$$\begin{bmatrix} 2 & 3 & -3 \\ 0 & -5 & 5 \\ 0 & 7 & -1 \\ 0 & -19 & 23 \end{bmatrix}$$ which is easier to manage.

Take any 3×3 sub matrix with the first row as it is:

for instance, $\begin{bmatrix} 2 & 3 & -3 \\ 0 & -5 & 5 \\ 0 & 7 & -1 \end{bmatrix}$

Its determinant is -60 which is not zero.

∴ rank is 3.

Example 3: Find the rank of the matrix $\begin{bmatrix} 1 & 0 & 1 & 1 \\ -1 & -2 & 1 & 3 \\ 3 & 2 & 1 & -1 \\ 1 & -4 & 5 & 9 \end{bmatrix}$

by use of elementary row and column transformation. First introduce zeros in the first column by multiplying the elements of the first row by suitable constants and adding them to the corresponding rows. Thus add the first two rows as they are, multiply by -3 the elements of the first row and add them to the third row and then multiply the first row by -1 and add them to the 4th row. The matrix is changed to an equivalent matrix.

$$\begin{bmatrix} 1 & 0 & 1 & 1 \\ 0 & -2 & 2 & 4 \\ 0 & 2 & -2 & -4 \\ 0 & -4 & 4 & 8 \end{bmatrix} \cong \begin{bmatrix} 1 & 0 & 1 & 1 \\ 0 & -2 & 2 & 4 \\ 0 & 0 & 0 & 0 \\ 0 & 0 & 0 & 0 \end{bmatrix}$$

Here we added (i) the 2nd and 3rd rows and (ii) multiplied by -2 the second row and added the elements to the 4th row.   This matrix takes the form $\begin{bmatrix} 1 & 0 & 0 & 0 \\ 0 & 1 & 0 & 0 \\ 0 & 0 & 0 & 0 \\ 0 & 0 & 0 & 0 \end{bmatrix}$ after

(i) multiplying the first column by -1 and adding the elements to the corresponding elements of the third and fourth columns, (ii) adding the elements of the second and third columns, (iii) multiplying the elements of the second column by 2 and adding them to the fourth column and lastly (iv) by multiplying the second row by $-\frac{1}{2}$. It is clearly seen that the determinant of the highest order which is not zero is

$\begin{vmatrix} 1 & 0 \\ 0 & 1 \end{vmatrix}$ $\therefore$ rank is 2.

Matrices form an important branch of Mathematics, with vast applications to statistics, modern Physics and Engineering. The rank of a matrix is required to treat systems of linear equations.

Exercise 8·3

Determine the rank of each of the following matrices, by using elementary transformations, wherever necessary.

1. $\begin{bmatrix} 3 & 5 & 7 \\ 18 & 30 & 42 \end{bmatrix}$

2. $\begin{bmatrix} 1 & 1 & 1 \\ 2 & 3 & 4 \\ 6 & 9 & 12 \end{bmatrix}$

3. $\begin{bmatrix} 1 & 0 & 0 \\ 0 & 1 & 0 \\ 0 & 0 & 1 \end{bmatrix}$

4. $\begin{bmatrix} 1 & 0 & 0 & 0 \\ 0 & 1 & 0 & 0 \\ 0 & 0 & 1 & 0 \end{bmatrix}$

5. $\begin{bmatrix} 6 & 8 & 2 \\ 21 & 9 & 17 \\ 3 & 4 & 1 \end{bmatrix}$

6. $\begin{bmatrix} 1 & 4 & 6 & 1 \\ 1 & -11 & -6 & 7 \\ 1 & -1 & 2 & 3 \end{bmatrix}$

7. $\begin{bmatrix} 1 & 2 & 4 \\ -2 & -3 & -1 \\ 0 & 1 & 7 \\ -2 & -2 & 6 \end{bmatrix}$

8. $\begin{bmatrix} -2 & -3 & -1 & 0 \\ 0 & 1 & 7 & -4 \\ 1 & 2 & 4 & -2 \end{bmatrix}$

9. $\begin{bmatrix} 2 & -2 & 0 & 6 \\ 4 & 2 & 0 & 2 \\ 1 & -1 & 0 & 3 \\ 1 & -2 & 1 & 2 \end{bmatrix}$ **10.** $\begin{bmatrix} 1 & 0 & 0 & 0 \\ -4 & -5 & 2 & 3 \\ -3 & -1 & 2 & 1 \\ 7 & 6 & -4 & 2 \end{bmatrix}$

11. $\begin{bmatrix} 4 & -2 & 1 & 3 \\ 2 & -1 & 3 & -2 \\ -2 & 3 & -2 & 1 \\ 3 & -3 & 2 & -2 \end{bmatrix}$ **12.** $\begin{bmatrix} 6 & 1 & 0 & 0 \\ 5 & 4 & -2 & 2 \\ -3 & 2 & 2 & 3 \\ 4 & -2 & 3 & 2 \end{bmatrix}$

13. $\begin{bmatrix} 1 & 7 & 17 & 3 \\ 10 & 18 & 40 & 17 \\ 4 & 8 & 18 & 7 \\ 0 & 4 & 10 & 1 \end{bmatrix}$ **14.** $\begin{bmatrix} 2 & -2 & -11 & 4 \\ -1 & 3 & 3 & 0 \\ 1 & -2 & -4 & 2 \\ 1 & -3 & -2 & 1 \end{bmatrix}$

15. Show that the matrix $\begin{bmatrix} 3 & 2 & 2 & 3 \\ 2 & -3 & 3 & 1 \\ 2 & 3 & -2 & -3 \end{bmatrix}$ can

be reduced to the form $\begin{bmatrix} 1 & 0 & 0 & -1 \\ 0 & 1 & 0 & 1 \\ 0 & 0 & 1 & 2 \end{bmatrix}$ by elemen-

tary transformations.

CHAPTER 9

Systems of Linear Equations

9.1. Systems of Linear Equations.

You are already familiar with solving two or three simultaneous equations in two or three unknowns. For instance, two simultaneous linear equations $a_{11}x + a_{12}y = a_{13}$ and $a_{21}x + a_{22}y = a_{23}$ have always a unique solution unless $\dfrac{a_{11}}{a_{21}} = \dfrac{a_{12}}{a_{22}}$. The two lines represented by the given equations are parallel and, therefore, do not meet in a point. Similarly a solution of three simultaneous linear equations can always be found unless the coefficients of x, y, z of any two equations are proportional. In the latter case, the two planes are ordinarily parallel and do not meet. Hence there are no common points. We can similarly deal with 4 simultaneous linear equations in four unknowns, 5 simultaneous linear equations in five unknowns and so on. If we are to expect a unique solution, the number of equations should ordinarily be the same as the number of unknowns and the coefficients of the unknowns should not be proportional. We may, however, have solutions even in cases where the number of equations is larger than the number of unknowns in special circumstances. It depends on the rank of the matrices formed of the coefficients of the equations.

9.2. Use of matrices in solving a system of linear equations.

To start with, we may consider two simultaneous equations which you have already done in school.

$$\left.\begin{array}{l} 3x + 4y = 2 \\ 2x - 3y = 7 \end{array}\right\} \quad \cdots\cdots (1)$$

By the usual method of elemination we find that $x=2$ and $y=-1$ are the solution equations.   ......(2)

The two equations (1) can be also written in the form of a product of two matrices equated to a zero matrix as under:

$$\begin{bmatrix} 3 & 4 & 2 \\ 2 & -3 & 7 \end{bmatrix} \times \begin{bmatrix} x \\ y \\ -1 \end{bmatrix} = \begin{bmatrix} 0 \\ 0 \end{bmatrix} ......(3)$$

The two matrices on the left side are (2×3) and (3×1), matrices respectively so that their multiplication is possible, as the number of columns in the first one is the same as the number of rows in the second. Similarly the solution equations can be put in the form

$$\begin{bmatrix} 1 & 0 & 2 \\ 0 & 1 & -1 \end{bmatrix} \times \begin{bmatrix} x \\ y \\ -1 \end{bmatrix} = \begin{bmatrix} 0 \\ 0 \end{bmatrix} ......(4)$$

as the equations (2) are $\quad 1{\cdot}x+0{\cdot}y = 2$
$$0{\cdot}x+1{\cdot}y = -1$$

Note that the elements in the first matrix on the left side of (3) are the detached coefficients of the equations since the first equation in (1) is $3x+4y=2$, we take 3, 4, 2 as the elements of the first row. To make it $3x+4y-2=0$ the element in the third row of the second matrix is -1. Thus according to the rule of multiplication of two matrices, the first set of equations in the form of matrices is $\begin{bmatrix} 3x+4y-2 \\ 2x-3y-7 \end{bmatrix} = \begin{bmatrix} 0 \\ 0 \end{bmatrix}$ and the second set is $\begin{bmatrix} x-2 \\ y+1 \end{bmatrix} = \begin{bmatrix} 0 \\ 0 \end{bmatrix}$. Equating the corresponding elements $3x+4y-2y$ and $2x-3y-7$ to zero, the solution equations are $x-2=0$ and $y+1-0$.

Further comparing the two matrices in the form of products (3) and (4), the matrix $\begin{bmatrix} 3 & 4 & 2 \\ 2 & -3 & 7 \end{bmatrix}$ and

$\begin{bmatrix} 1 & 0 & 2 \\ 0 & 1 & -1 \end{bmatrix}$ must be equivalent, as they lead to the same solutions. This is easily seen to be true from the following elementary transformations (see section 8·5 of the previous chapter.)

$\begin{bmatrix} 3 & 4 & 2 \\ 2 & -3 & 7 \end{bmatrix} \cong \begin{bmatrix} 6 & 8 & 4 \\ 6 & -9 & 21 \end{bmatrix}$ multiplying the first row by 2 and the second one by 3.

$\cong \begin{bmatrix} 6 & 8 & 4 \\ 0 & -17 & 17 \end{bmatrix}$ by deducting the first row from the second.

$\cong \begin{bmatrix} 6 & 8 & 4 \\ 0 & -1 & 1 \end{bmatrix}$ by dividing the second row by 17.

$\cong \begin{bmatrix} 6 & 8 & 4 \\ 0 & -8 & 8 \end{bmatrix}$ by multiplying the second row by 8.

$\cong \begin{bmatrix} 6 & 0 & 12 \\ 0 & -8 & 8 \end{bmatrix}$ by adding the second row to the first one.

$\cong \begin{bmatrix} 1 & 0 & 2 \\ 0 & 1 & -1 \end{bmatrix}$ by dividing the first row by 6 and the second one by -8.

So we see that the first matrix on the left side of (3) is equivalent to the first matrix of the left side of (4). The matrix containing only the coefficients of the unknowns is called the *matrix of coefficients*, while the matrix containing the coefficients as well as the numbers on the right sides of the equations is called the *augmented matrix*. Thus in the above example

$\begin{bmatrix} 3 & 4 \\ 2 & -3 \end{bmatrix}$ is the coefficient matrix,

while $\begin{bmatrix} 3 & 4 & 2 \\ 2 & -3 & 7 \end{bmatrix}$ is the augmented matrix.

Similarly in the case of three equations like

$$a_{11}x + a_{12}y + a_{13}z = b_1$$
$$a_{21}x + a_{22}y + a_{23}z = b_2$$
$$a_{31}x + a_{32}y + a_{33}z = b_3,$$

the coefficient matrix is   the augmented matrix is

$$\begin{bmatrix} a_{11} & a_{12} & a_{13} \\ a_{21} & a_{22} & a_{23} \\ a_{31} & a_{32} & a_{33} \end{bmatrix} \text{ and } \begin{bmatrix} a_{11} & a_{12} & a_{13} & b_1 \\ a_{21} & a_{22} & a_{23} & b_2 \\ a_{31} & a_{32} & a_{33} & b_3 \end{bmatrix}.$$

One of the methods of solving a system of simultaneous linear equations is to convert the augmented matrix of the equations into a form like this:

$$\begin{bmatrix} 1 & 0 & 0 & 0 & \ldots\ldots k_1 \\ 0 & 1 & 0 & 0 & \ldots\ldots k_2 \\ 0 & 0 & 1 & 0 & \ldots\ldots k_3 \\ & & \text{etc.} & & \end{bmatrix}$$

This gives the solutions $x=k_1$, $y=k_2$, $z=k_3$ etc. Note that the elementary transformations applied to the augmented matrix really amount to the method of elimination we are accustomed to in the school algebra. This will be clear from the following illustrated examples.

Example 1 : Solve the simultaneous system

$$\begin{rcases} x+2y+3z=6 \\ 2x+\ y-\ z=-3 \\ 3x-\ y+2z=11 \end{rcases} \text{ or } \begin{bmatrix} 1 & 2 & 3 & 6 \\ 2 & 1 & -1 & -3 \\ 3 & -1 & 2 & 11 \end{bmatrix} \cdot \begin{bmatrix} x \\ y \\ z \\ -1 \end{bmatrix} = \begin{bmatrix} 0 \\ 0 \\ 0 \end{bmatrix}.$$

We solve this system by reducing the augmented matrix to the form indicated above as well as by the usual method of elimination.

Elimination method.

Add -2 times the first eqn., to the second eqn. and -3 times the first eqn. to the third one. The equation will then be.

$1 \cdot x + 2y + 3z = 6$
$0 \cdot x - 3y - 7z = -15$
$0 \cdot x - 7y - 7z = -7$

Augmented matrix:

Add -2 times the first row to the second row and -3 times the first row to the third one.

$$\begin{bmatrix} 1 & 2 & 3 & 6 \\ 0 & -3 & -7 & -15 \\ 0 & -7 & -7 & -7 \end{bmatrix}$$

M. C. A. (III)—5

Change the negative sign in the second equation or row by multiplying by (-1) throughout. Also divide the last equation or row by -7 throughout. Now the set of equations and the matrix will be

$1 \cdot x + 2y + 3z = 6$
$0 \cdot x + 3y + 7z = 15$
$0 \cdot x + y + z = 1$

$$\begin{bmatrix} 1 & 2 & 3 & 6 \\ 0 & 3 & 7 & 15 \\ 0 & 1 & 1 & 1 \end{bmatrix}$$

Multiply the third eqn. by -3 and add the second eqn. to it.

Multiply the third row by -3 and add the second row to it. Thus it will be

$1 \cdot x + 2y + 3z = 6$
$0 \cdot x + 3y + 7z = 15$
$0 \cdot x + 0 \cdot y + 4z = 12$

$$\begin{bmatrix} 1 & 2 & 3 & 6 \\ 0 & 3 & 7 & 15 \\ 0 & 0 & 4 & 12 \end{bmatrix}$$

The equation may be written now by dividing the last equation by 4.

The last row gives $4z = 12$ or $z = 3$. The matrix may be written now by dividing the last row by 4.

$1 \cdot x + 2y + 3z = 6$
$0 \cdot x + 3y + 7z = 15$
$0 \cdot x + 0 \cdot y + z = 3$

$$\begin{bmatrix} 1 & 2 & 3 & 6 \\ 0 & 3 & 7 & 15 \\ 0 & 0 & 1 & 3 \end{bmatrix}$$

Adding -7 times the last equation to the second eqn.

Now multiply the last row by -7 and add to the second row

$1 \cdot x + 2y + 3z = 6$
$0 \cdot x + 3y + 0 \cdot z = -6$
$0 \cdot x + 0 \cdot y + 1 \cdot z = 3$

$$\begin{bmatrix} 1 & 2 & 3 & 6 \\ 0 & 3 & 0 & -6 \\ 0 & 0 & 1 & 3 \end{bmatrix} \quad \text{or}$$

This gives $3y = -6$ or $y = -2$. The equation can be written as

$x + 2y + 3z = 6$
$\quad\quad y \quad\quad = -2$
$\quad\quad\quad\quad z = 3$

$$\begin{bmatrix} 1 & 2 & 3 & 6 \\ 0 & 1 & 0 & -2 \\ 0 & 0 & 1 & 3 \end{bmatrix}$$

by dividing the second row by 3.

Multiply the second eqn. by -2 and the third one by -3 and add them to the first.

Multiply the second row by -2 and the third one by -3 and add them to the first row.

Now the system of equations and matrix will be as under:

$$\begin{aligned} x &&&= 1 \\ & y &&= -2 \\ && z &= 3 \end{aligned} \qquad \begin{bmatrix} 1 & 0 & 0 & 1 \\ 0 & 1 & 0 & -2 \\ 0 & 0 & 1 & 3 \end{bmatrix}$$

Since the first three elements of each row are the co-efficients of x, y, z respectively, $x=1$, $y=-2$ and $z=3$.

It is usual to state the results as $(x, y, z) = (1, -2, 3)$. The coefficient matrix is a unit matrix. If we remember that the elements of the augmented matrix stand for detached coefficients of the unknowns, it will be obvious that we should apply elementary transformations to the *rows only* and not to *columns*. Such a transformation to columns will upset the system of equations, and the solutions will not be the ones required. Note the analogy between the equations and the matrix.

1. The order in which the equations are written is immaterial. Similarly any two rows may be interchanged.

2. Any equations may be multiplied by the same non-zero constant.

3. k times the members of an equation may be added to (or subtracted from) the corresponding members of another equation. Similarly k times the elements of a row of a matrix may be added to or subtracted from the corresponding elements of another row.

Example 2: Solve

$$\begin{aligned} 2x + 3y - 4z &= 9 \\ 5x + 2y + 5z &= 13 \\ 7x + 5y + z &= 5. \end{aligned}$$

The coefficient matrix is

$$\begin{bmatrix} 2 & 3 & -4 \\ 5 & 2 & 5 \\ 7 & 5 & 1 \end{bmatrix} \cong \begin{bmatrix} 2 & 3 & -4 \\ 7 & 5 & 1 \\ 7 & 5 & 1 \end{bmatrix} \cong \begin{bmatrix} 2 & 3 & -4 \\ 7 & 5 & 1 \\ 0 & 0 & 0 \end{bmatrix}$$

The rank of the coefficient matrix is 2 (which is less than 3). The second matrix is obtained by adding the first two rows and third one by subtracting the second row from the third one. The given equations can be put in the form

$$\begin{bmatrix} 2 & 3 & -4 & 9 \\ 5 & 2 & 5 & 13 \\ 7 & 5 & 1 & 5 \end{bmatrix} \times \begin{bmatrix} x \\ y \\ z \\ -1 \end{bmatrix} = \begin{bmatrix} 0 \\ 0 \\ 0 \end{bmatrix}$$

or $$\begin{bmatrix} 2 & 3 & -4 & 9 \\ 7 & 5 & 1 & 22 \\ 0 & 0 & 0 & -17 \end{bmatrix} \times \begin{bmatrix} x \\ y \\ z \\ -1 \end{bmatrix} = \begin{bmatrix} 0 \\ 0 \\ 0 \end{bmatrix}.$$

This leads to the absurd result $17 = 0$. Hence the system has no solution.

Example 3: Solve the simultaneous system

$$x - 2y + 3z = 11$$
$$3x + y - z = 2$$
$$5x + 3y + 2z = 3.$$

The augmented matrix is $$\begin{bmatrix} 1 & -2 & 3 & 11 \\ 3 & 1 & -1 & 2 \\ 5 & 3 & 2 & 3 \end{bmatrix}$$

$$= \begin{bmatrix} 1 & -2 & 3 & 11 \\ 0 & 7 & -10 & -31 \\ 0 & 13 & -13 & -52 \end{bmatrix} \cong \begin{bmatrix} 1 & -2 & 3 & 11 \\ 0 & 1 & -1 & -4 \\ 0 & 7 & -10 & -31 \end{bmatrix}$$

by carrying out the usual transformation viz. multiply the 1st row by 3 and subtract from the second row and multiply the 1st row by 5 and subtract from the third row. Then interchange the 2nd and 3rd rows and multiply the new second row by $\frac{1}{13}$.

Now multiply the second row by 7 and subtract from the third row. The new matrix is, after dividing the third row by -3,

$$\begin{bmatrix} 1 & -2 & 3 & 11 \\ 0 & 1 & -1 & -4 \\ 0 & 0 & -3 & -3 \end{bmatrix} \cong \begin{bmatrix} 1 & -2 & 3 & 11 \\ 0 & 1 & -1 & -4 \\ 0 & 0 & 1 & 1 \end{bmatrix}.$$

We can now rewrite the equation using the new matrix

$$\begin{bmatrix} 1 & -2 & 3 & 11 \\ 0 & 1 & -1 & -4 \\ 0 & 0 & 1 & 1 \end{bmatrix} \cdot \begin{bmatrix} x \\ y \\ z \\ -1 \end{bmatrix} = \begin{bmatrix} 0 \\ 0 \\ 0 \end{bmatrix} \quad \text{or}$$

$$\begin{aligned} x - 2y + 3z - 11 &= 0 \\ y - z + 4 &= 0 \\ z - 1 &= 0 \end{aligned}$$

A system of this type of equations is called a *triangular form* and may be solved easily.

$z = 1$ from the third equation.

$y = -3$ from the second equation.

$x = 2$ from the first equation.

Example 4: Solve the simultaneous system

$$\begin{aligned} -2x + 4y + 2z &= -2 \\ 2x + 3y - 3z &= -7 \\ 3x + 2y - 2z &= -3 \\ 5x - 2y + 4z &= 15. \end{aligned}$$

We note that there are four equations in three unknowns. We shall have a unique solution for x, y and z if the rank of the matrix of coefficients and that of the augmented matrix is 3. The augmented matrix with the second row taken first is

$$\begin{bmatrix} 2 & 3 & -3 & -7 \\ -2 & 4 & 2 & -2 \\ 3 & 2 & -2 & -3 \\ 5 & -2 & 4 & 15 \end{bmatrix} \cong \begin{bmatrix} 2 & 3 & -3 & -7 \\ 0 & 7 & -1 & -9 \\ 0 & 5 & -5 & -15 \\ 0 & 19 & -23 & -65 \end{bmatrix}$$

Adding the 1st and 2nd row, subtracting 2 times the 3rd row from 3 times the first row etc. Divide the third by 5.

$$\cong \begin{bmatrix} 2 & 3 & -3 & -7 \\ 0 & 7 & -1 & -9 \\ 0 & 1 & -1 & -3 \\ 0 & 19 & -23 & -65 \end{bmatrix} \cong \begin{bmatrix} 2 & 3 & -3 & -7 \\ 0 & 0 & 6 & 12 \\ 0 & 1 & -1 & -3 \\ 0 & 0 & -4 & -8 \end{bmatrix}$$

Multiply 3rd row by 7 and subtract it from the second row,

multiply the third row by 19 and subtract from the fourth row etc.

$$\cong \begin{bmatrix} 2 & 3 & -3 & -7 \\ 0 & 0 & 1 & 2 \\ 0 & 1 & -1 & -3 \\ 0 & 0 & 1 & 2 \end{bmatrix}$$

$$\therefore \quad 2x+3y-3z = -7$$
$$z = 2$$
$$y-z = -3$$

$$\therefore \quad z=2, \ y=-1, \text{ and } x=2.$$

Notice that two rows viz. the second and the fourth are identical. Hence the rank of the matrix is 3.

There is one surplus equation with the same values of x, y, z satisfying it and, therefore, the equations are not inconsistent.

Example 5: Solve the system:

$$x + 2y + z \qquad = 2$$
$$2x \qquad - 2z + t = 6$$
$$4y + 3z + 2t = -1$$
$$-x + 6y - z - t = 2$$

There are four equations in four unknowns. We follow the same method, viz. introduce three 0s in the first column by suitable multiplications and additions of rows, then two 0s in the second column and one 0 in the third column in the augmented matrix.

$$\begin{bmatrix} 1 & 2 & 1 & 0 & 2 \\ 2 & 0 & -2 & 1 & 6 \\ 0 & 4 & 3 & 2 & -1 \\ -1 & 6 & -1 & -1 & 2 \end{bmatrix} \cong \begin{bmatrix} 1 & 2 & 1 & 0 & 2 \\ 0 & -4 & -4 & 1 & 2 \\ 0 & 4 & 3 & 2 & -1 \\ 0 & 8 & 0 & -1 & 4 \end{bmatrix}$$

$$\cong \begin{bmatrix} 1 & 2 & 1 & 0 & 2 \\ 0 & -4 & -4 & 1 & 2 \\ 0 & 0 & -1 & 3 & 1 \\ 0 & 0 & -8 & 1 & 8 \end{bmatrix} \cong \begin{bmatrix} 1 & 2 & 1 & 0 & 2 \\ 0 & -4 & -4 & 1 & 2 \\ 0 & 0 & -1 & 3 & 1 \\ 0 & 0 & 0 & -23 & 0 \end{bmatrix}$$

Step 1: Multiply the first row by −2 and add to the second row. Add the first and the fourth rows. We have now 3 0^s in the first column.

Step 2: Add second and third rows to introduce 0 in the third row. Multiply the second row by 2 and add to the fourth row.

Step 3: Multiply the third row by −8 and add to the fourth row. Now we have reduced the equation to the triangular form. At this stage we can solve the equations, as the last row gives $−23 t=0$ or $t=0$ and we can work backwards $−z+3t=1$ or $z=−1$. The second row then gives $−4y−4z+t=2$ or $y=\frac{1}{2}$. The first row gives $x+2y+z=2$ or $x=2$.

If we want to change at this stage the coefficients matrix into the unit or identity matrix i.e. have 1^s in the diagonal and 0$_s$ elsewhere, we can easily do. Dividing the last by −23 the augmented matrix is

$$\begin{bmatrix} 1 & 2 & 1 & 0 & 2 \\ 0 & -4 & -4 & 1 & 1 \\ 0 & 0 & -1 & 3 & 1 \\ 0 & 0 & 0 & 1 & 0 \end{bmatrix} \cong \begin{bmatrix} 1 & 2 & 1 & 0 & 2 \\ 0 & -4 & -4 & 1 & 2 \\ 0 & 0 & 1 & 0 & -1 \\ 0 & 0 & 0 & 1 & 0 \end{bmatrix}$$

by adding −3 times the fourth row to the 3rd row and changing the signs.

$$\cong \begin{bmatrix} 1 & 2 & 1 & 0 & 2 \\ 0 & -4 & 0 & 0 & -2 \\ 0 & 0 & 1 & 0 & -1 \\ 0 & 0 & 0 & 1 & 0 \end{bmatrix} \cong \begin{bmatrix} 1 & 2 & 1 & 0 & 2 \\ 0 & 1 & 0 & 0 & \frac{1}{2} \\ 0 & 0 & 1 & 0 & -1 \\ 0 & 0 & 0 & 1 & 0 \end{bmatrix}$$

by adding −1 times the fourth row and 4 times the third row to the second row. Divide the second row by −4.

$$\cong \begin{bmatrix} 1 & 0 & 0 & 0 & 2 \\ 0 & 1 & 0 & 0 & \frac{1}{2} \\ 0 & 0 & 1 & 0 & -1 \\ 0 & 0 & 0 & 1 & 0 \end{bmatrix}$$

by subtracting the third row from the first and then 2 times the 2nd row from the first.

Now the coefficient matrix (that is the matrix of elements leaving the last column) has been turned into I, the identity matrix with 1 in the diagonal and 0s elsewhere. The advantage of this form is that we recognise the solution at once $x=2, y=\frac{1}{2}, z=-1$ and $t=0$.

A non-singular square matrix can be reduced by means of elementary transformations to an identity matrix having 1s along the diagonal and 0s elsewhere. The matrix method may be applied even to a system of equations where the number of equations is less than the number of unknowns.

Example 6: Solve, if possible, the following system of equations by using elementary transformations.

$$\begin{aligned} x + 2y - 2z + 3t &= -3 \\ 2x + 4y - 5z + 6t &= -1 \\ -x - 2y \qquad\quad - 3t &= 15 \end{aligned}$$

The augmented matrix is

$$\begin{bmatrix} 1 & 2 & -2 & 3 & -3 \\ 2 & 4 & -5 & 6 & -1 \\ -1 & -2 & 0 & -3 & 15 \end{bmatrix} \cong \begin{bmatrix} 1 & 2 & -2 & 3 & -3 \\ 0 & 0 & -1 & 0 & 5 \\ 0 & 0 & -2 & 0 & 12 \end{bmatrix}$$

$$\cong \begin{bmatrix} 1 & 2 & -2 & 3 & -3 \\ 0 & 0 & -1 & 0 & 5 \\ 0 & 0 & 0 & 0 & 2 \end{bmatrix}$$

1st step: Multiply the first row by 2 and deduct the elements from those of the second row. Add 1st and 3rd rows.

2nd step: Multiply the second row by -2 and add to the third row.

Now the equations are equivalent to

$$\begin{aligned} x+2y-2z+3t &= -3 \\ -z &= 5 \\ 0 &= 2 \end{aligned}$$

∴ the system is inconsistent.

Note that here the rank of the coefficient matrix is 2 while that of the augmented matrix is 3.

9.3. General Linear systems.

In general we can consider a system of m linear equations in n unknowns, where m may not be the same as n. They may be written as

$$a_{11}\ x_1 + a_{12}\ x_2 + \ldots\ldots + a_{1n}\ x_n = b_1$$
$$a_{21}\ x_1 + a_{22}\ x_2 + \ldots\ldots + a_{2n}\ x_n = b_2$$
$$\ldots\ldots\ldots\ldots\ldots\ldots\ldots\ldots\ldots\ldots\ldots\ldots\ldots\ldots$$
$$a_{m1}\ x_1 + a_{m2}\ x_2 + \ldots\ldots + m_{mn}\ x_n = b_m$$

In this system we denote the $m \times n$ matrix

$$A = \begin{bmatrix} a_{11} & a_{12} & \ldots\ldots & a_{1n} \\ a_{21} & a_{22} & \ldots\ldots & a_{2n} \\ \ldots & \ldots & \ldots\ldots & \ldots \\ a_{m1} & a_{m2} & \ldots\ldots & a_{mn} \end{bmatrix}$$

This is known as the *coefficient matrix* while

$$B = \begin{bmatrix} a_{11} & a_{12} & \ldots\ldots & a_{1n} & b_1 \\ a_{21} & a_{22} & \ldots\ldots & a_{2n} & b_2 \\ \ldots & \ldots & \ldots\ldots & \ldots \\ a_{m1} & a_{m2} & \ldots\ldots & a_{mn} & b_m \end{bmatrix}$$

is known as the *augmented matrix*. B is an $m \times (n+1)$ matrix.

Suppose we reduce the augmented matrix by means of elementary transformations described in section 8·5 of the previous chapter. First we notice that such transformations reduce the coefficient matrix simultaneously. Secondly the interchange of the two rows of a matrix corresponds to the change of two rows of the system of equations. Multiplication of a row by a constant is the same thing as multiplication of an equation by a constant and also has no effect on the solution. Multiplying a row by a constant and adding the result to another row is the same as multiplying an equation by a constant and adding the result to another equation. By this also, the solution is not affected. For instance, in two simultaneous equations

$$ax + by + c = 0 \text{ and}$$
$$a'x + b'y + c' = 0$$

the values of x and y which satisfy the two equations also satisfy the equations $ax+by+c+k(a'x+b'y+c')=0$. Such transformations, therefore, do not affect the solutions of the given equations. Suppose B is the augmented matrix of a certain system of equation and B' is obtained from B by applying a finite number of elementary transformations *involving only rows* as described above. Then B and B' are equivalent matrices and the system of equations corresponding to B and B' are the same.

As we have seen earlier, B and B' have the same rank. In Linear Algebra, the rank of a matrix plays an important part. We shall consider the various types of linear equations.

Case 1: If $m=n$, then there are n linear equations in n variables. This is the most straight-forward case. If the coefficient matrix and the augmented matrix have the same rank equal to n, the solution is unique. [see the illustrated examples 1, 2, 3.]

Case 2: If $m<n$, there are fewer equations than the unknowns. This is the case of surplus unknowns. If r is the rank of the coefficient matrix as well as of the augmented matrix, we can solve for r unknowns in terms of the remaining $n-r$ unknowns.

Example
$$2x + 4y + z = -1$$
$$x + 2y + 2z = 1$$

Here the rank of the coefficient matrix is 2 and that of the augmented matrix is also 2. So we can solve for 2 unknowns in terms of the third unknown.

$$\begin{bmatrix} 2 & 4 & 1 & -1 \\ 1 & 2 & 2 & 1 \end{bmatrix} \cong \begin{bmatrix} 2 & 4 & 1 & -1 \\ 0 & 0 & 3 & 3 \end{bmatrix} \cong \begin{bmatrix} 2 & 4 & 1 & -1 \\ 0 & 0 & 1 & 1 \end{bmatrix}$$

$$\therefore z = 1$$

The other equation is $2x+4y+1=-1$

or $x+2y=-1$ if we treat y as surplus.

$\therefore x=-(1+2y)$ or if we treat x as surplus

$$y=-\tfrac{1}{2}(1+x).$$

Case 3: If $n < m$, there are fewer unknowns than equations. If the rank of the two matrices is r, solution is possible if the surplus $m - r$ equations are dependent equations. The latter equations can be ignored.

[See example 4 illustrated.]

Exercise

Use the matrix method to solve the following systems of equations:

1. $5x + 2y = 7.$
$3x + y = 4$

2. $9x - 5y = 33.$
$5x + 9y = -17$

3. $x - y + 2z = -2$
$2y - 3z = 2$
$3x - 2y + 4z = -5$

4. $x + y + z = 2$
$2x - y + 3z = 8$
$3x + 2y - z = 3.$

5. $x + y - 5z = 8$
$x + 2y + z = 3$
$x + 3y + 7z = -2.$

6. $6x - 2y - 2z = -1$
$2x + y + 4z = 0$
$4x + 3y + 5z = 0.$

7. $x + 4y - 2z = 3$
$x + 5y = 1$
$-x - y + 8z = -6.$

8. $x + y - 3z = -2$
$x + y + z = 0$
$2x - y + 4z = 3.$

9. $x + 3y + 2z = 5$
$2x + y + z = 3$
$5x + 2y + 3z = 6.$

10. $2x + y - 3z = 7$
$x + 3y + 4z = 11$
$4x + 2y - 6z = 14.$

11. $2x + 3y - z = -15$
$3x + 5y + 2z = 0$
$x + 3y + 3z = 11$
$7x + 11y = -30.$

12. $x + 2y - z = 3$
$2x - y - 2z = 5$
$3x + y - 3z = 8.$

13. $2x + y + z = 7$
$x - y + 4z = 11.$

14. $3x + y + 2z = 9$
$x - 3y + 5z = 4$
$2x + 4y - 3z = 7.$

15. $x - y + 2z + w = -3$
$2x + y - z - w = 8$
$2x + 2y + 3z + w = 1$
$-x + y - 2z + 3w = -5.$

16. $x + 2y + 3z + t = 6$
$y + 2z + 3t = 3$
$3x - y + z = 2$
$3x + 2y - t = 5.$

17.
$$-2x+ y+ z+3t = 0$$
$$3x+ y- z = 0$$
$$2x-2y- z+6t = 4$$
$$4x- y-2z-3t = 0$$

18.
$$3x+2y -4t = 0$$
$$y-2z+ t = -1$$
$$2x+3y = 1$$
$$x +4z-2t = 2.$$

19.
$$2x+3y+z+ t = 1$$
$$3x+ y+z+2t = 0$$
$$x -z+ t = 2$$
$$x- y-z+ t = 1$$

20.
$$x+2y-2z+3w-4t = -3$$
$$2x+4y-5z+6w-5t = -1$$
$$x+2y +3w-11t = -15.$$

CHAPTER 10

Infinite Series

10.1. Infinite sequences.

The set of numbers 3, 5, 7, 9, ... 61 forms a *sequence* of 30 numbers. They have been arranged in a definite order so that we can say exactly where a particular term comes. They form an arithmetic progression and there are exactly 30 terms. The rule for finding a particular term is $3+2(n-1)$ or $2n+1$. Thus 10th term is 21, the first term is $2+1$ or 3 and the last term $2\times30+1$ or 61. Since this set of numbers contains both a first and a last term, the sequence is called *finite*. Another example of a finite sequence is a set of numbers 1, -2, 3, -4, 5, ... 100. There are exactly 100 terms in the sequence. Here also each member of the set occupies a definite place in the set. If we know the position of a particular term, we can find it and conversely if we know a particular member of the sequence, we can find its position by the formula $(-1)^{n-1}n$. In general a sequence is written u_1, u_2, u_3, u_4, ... u_n or briefly $\{u_n\}$. Since such a sequence of numbers stops somewhere, it is called a *finite sequence*. A finite sequence has both a first and a last element. On the other hand, if the sequence does not stop and continues indefinitely, it has no last term. Such a sequence is called an *infinite sequence*. For example, the sequence 1, $\frac{1}{2}$, $\frac{1}{2^2}$, $\frac{1}{2^3}$ ...... is an infinite sequence, as there is no last term. The dots indicate that the sequence is unending. For every sequence there is a rule or a formula for finding out any member of the sequence. The general term is a function of the integer n. For instance, in the sequence $\left\{\dfrac{1}{2^n}\right\}$ the position of any term is uniquely known if we know n. Thus a sequence is a function the domain of which is a part or the whole of the set of the positive integers. The range may be any part of the real number system. We can denote the sequence by the symbol $\{(n, f(n)) \mid n = 1, 2, 3, \ldots\ldots\}$ just to remind ourselves of the fact that it is a function of n. The following are some simple examples of an infinite sequence:

(a) $1, \frac{1}{2}, \frac{1}{3}, \frac{1}{4} \ldots \dfrac{1}{n}, \ldots\ldots$

Here u_n of $f(n) = \dfrac{1}{n}$. $f(1) = 1, f(2) = \frac{1}{2}, f(3) = \frac{1}{3}$ and so on.

(b) $1, \frac{1}{2}, \dfrac{1}{2^2}, \dfrac{1}{2^3}, \ldots\ldots \dfrac{1}{2^{n-1}} \ldots\ldots$

Here u_n or $f(n) = \dfrac{1}{2^{n-1}}$ (a function of n).

$f(1) = 1, f(2) = \frac{1}{2}, f(3) = \dfrac{1}{2^2}, \ldots f(n) = \dfrac{1}{2^{n-1}}$

(c) $\frac{1}{2}, \frac{2}{3}, \frac{3}{4}, \frac{4}{5}, \ldots\ldots \dfrac{n}{n+1}, \ldots\ldots$

Here u_n or $f(n) = \dfrac{n}{n+1}$, $f(1) = \frac{1}{2}$, $f(2) = \frac{2}{3}$, $f(3) = \frac{3}{4}$ and so on.

(d) $3, 6, 9, 12, \ldots\ldots 3n \ldots\ldots$

Here u_n or $f(n) = 3n$, so that $f(1) = 3, f(2) = 6, f(3) = 9$ etc.

10.2. Upper and lower bounds.

Consider the ordered set of rational numbers $1, \frac{1}{10}$, $\dfrac{1}{10^2}, \dfrac{1}{10^3} \ldots\ldots, \dfrac{1}{10^9}$. These ten numbers have been arranged in a descending order, that is, each is less than its predecessor.

It has a first term and a last term. Each one of them is $\leqslant 1$ and $\geqslant \dfrac{1}{10^9}$. We may say that 1 is an upper bound and $\dfrac{1}{10^9}$ is a lower bound of this set.

Now consider the sequence $\left\{\dfrac{1}{10^{n+1}}\right\}$. When we write it more elaborately, it will be $\left\{1, \tfrac{1}{10}, \dfrac{1}{10^2}, \ \cdots\cdots \ \dfrac{1}{10^n} \cdots\right\}$. Let us call this set of numbers S.

Each element of the set $\leqslant 1$ and $\geqslant 0$. So 1 and 0 are upper and lower bounds.

Definition: The number v is alled an upper bound of a set S if each element of $S \leqslant v$. Similarly the number u is called a lower bound of a set S if each element of $S \geqslant u$.

It is easily seen that according to this definition, there are many upper bounds and many lower bounds for each set of numbers. In the above example, the sequence $\left\{\dfrac{1}{10^{n+1}}\right\}$ has 1, 2, $2\tfrac{1}{2}$, 3 $\ \ldots\ldots$ as upper bounds and 0, $-\tfrac{1}{2}$, $-\tfrac{1}{3}$, -1 $\ldots.$ as lower bounds.

Our main interest is to emphasise the smallest of the upper bounds and the largest of the lower bounds. The smallest of the upper bounds of A in the case above is 1 and the largest of the lower bounds of B is 0.

Postulate: Every set S where $S \subset R$ and has an upper bound has a least upper bound. Similarly, every set S that has a lower bound has a greatest lower bound. R is the set of real numbers.

Actually when we talk of *the* upper and lower bounds of a sequence or of a set, we mean the smallest of the upper bounds and the largest of the lower bounds as defined above. The upper bound M of a sequence is defined by the following properties:

(i) Every element of the sequence $\{u_n\} \leqslant M$.

(ii) There is at least one element of the sequence $> M - \epsilon$ where ϵ is any given small number $\epsilon > 0$.

The lower bound m of a sequence is similarly defined as under:

(i) Every element of the sequence $\geqslant m$ and

(ii) there is at least one element of the sequence $< m + \epsilon$, where ϵ is any given small number $\epsilon > 0$.

The least upper bound and the greatest lower bound may or may not be in the sequence.

The set $1, \frac{1}{2}, \frac{1}{3}, \ldots \ldots \frac{1}{n}, \ldots \ldots$

1 as its upper bound, while its lower bound is 0.

If $\epsilon = \frac{1}{1000}$, there is an element $\frac{1}{1001} < \epsilon$

Similarly the element $1 > 1 - \frac{1}{1000}$

$\therefore$ 1 is *the* uppr bound and 0 is *the* lower bound. 1 is in the sequence, while 0 is not. In the set $S = \{x \mid a < x < b\}$, b is the upper bound and a is the lower bound. The upper bound means the least upper bound and the lower bound means the greatest lower bound.

Example: Show that the set of positive integers I has no upper bound.

If I has an upper bound, it has a least upper bound M by the postulate given above such that every element of $I \leqslant M$. But it is always possible to find an integer n such that $n > M$. $\therefore$ our assumption that I has an upper bound is wrong.

Exercise (For discussion).

1. By the usual definition show that in the set $\{x \mid a < x < b\}$, a is the lower bound and b is the upper bound.

2. Give an example of a subset of R such that

   (i) it has neither an upper bound nor a lower bound,

   (ii) it has an upper bound but no lower bound,

   (iii) it does not contain its upper and lower bounds,

   (iv) it contians both its upper and lower bounds.

3. Find the upper and lower bounds of the following sets if they exist:

   (a) $\{x \mid x \in R \quad \text{and} \quad x > 3\}$

   (b) $\{x \mid x \in Q \quad \text{and} \quad x^2 > 3\}$

   (c) $\{x \mid x \in I \quad \text{and} \quad -2 \leqslant x < 1\}$.

4. Prove that the set $\{-1, 0, 1, 2\}$ contains its upper and lower bounds.

5. Find the upper and lower bounds of

$$\tfrac{1}{2}, \ \tfrac{2}{3}, \ \tfrac{3}{4}, \ \tfrac{4}{5}, \ \tfrac{5}{6}, \ \ldots\ldots$$

10.3. The limit of an infinite sequence.

Definition. Given the infinite sequence $u_1, u_2, \ldots u_n,$ $\ldots\ldots$, we say that the sequence has the limit l if, for a given ϵ, however small, there is a positive integer N such that u_n lies between $l - \epsilon$ and $l + \epsilon$ for all $n > N$.

Here N depends on ϵ (a given small positive number). We also write $u_n \longrightarrow l$ as $n \longrightarrow \infty$ or $\lim\limits_{n \to \infty} u_n = l$. Consider the examples (a), (b), (c), (d) given above.

   (a) Here $u_n = \dfrac{1}{n}$ and let $\epsilon = \tfrac{1}{100}$. We can easily show that u_n lies between $-\tfrac{1}{100}$ and $+\tfrac{1}{100}$ for all $n > 100$. Actually $u_n < \tfrac{1}{10}$ and $> -\tfrac{1}{100}$ for all $n > 100$. Hence for a given ϵ, we can find an N (here it is 100) such that $|u_n| < \epsilon$ for all $n > N$.

Hence l or the limit of u_n is 0.

If $\epsilon = \tfrac{1}{10000}$, $N = 10,000$ and so on.

(b) u_n here is $\dfrac{1}{2^{n-1}}$. If $\epsilon = \frac{1}{100}$, $\mathcal{N}=8$

as $\dfrac{1}{2^7} = \frac{1}{128} < \frac{1}{100}$.

Here also $\lim\limits_{n \to \infty} u_n = 0$. The sequence has the limit 0.

(c) Here $u_n = \dfrac{n}{n+1} = 1 - \dfrac{1}{n+1}$. As in (a),

$\dfrac{1}{n+1} \to 0$ as $n \to \infty$.

$\therefore \lim\limits_{n \to \infty} u_n = 1$

We can verify our definition of a limit.

If $\epsilon = \frac{1}{100}$, $\mathcal{N}=100$,

$1 - \frac{1}{100} < u_n < 1 + \frac{1}{100}$ for all $n > 100$.

This can be written also as $|\,u_n - 1\,| < \epsilon$ for all $n > 100$.

(d) Here $u_n = 3n$. This sequence goes on increasing as n increases. There is no number l such that we can find an $\mathcal{N}$ for which $|\,3n - l\,| < \epsilon$ for all $n > \mathcal{N}$ for a given $\epsilon > 0$. Hence there is no finite limit for this sequence. In fact, u_n can be made larger than any given integer, however large it may be, by giving n a sufficiently large value. Its limit is infinity. We say $u_n \to \infty$, as $n \to \infty$.

10.4. Theorems on limits.

Theorem 1 : If $\lim\limits_{n \to \infty} u_n = u$ and $\lim\limits_{n \to \infty} v_n = v$,

then (a) $\lim\limits_{n \to \infty} (u_n + v_n) = u + v$

(b) $\lim\limits_{n \to \infty} (u_n - v_n) = u - v$

(c) $\lim_{n \to \infty} (u_n \cdot v_n) = u \cdot v$

(d) $\lim_{n \to \infty} \dfrac{u_n}{v_n} = \dfrac{u}{v}$ provided $v \neq 0$.

These results are proved in books on Calculus.

Theorem 2: If an infinite sequence u_1, u_2, ... has the property that (i) $u_{n+1} \geqslant u_n$ for all n, and (ii) there is a number m such that $u_n \leqslant m$ for all n, then there is a number $b \leqslant m$ such that $\lim_{n \to \infty} u_n = b$ and $u_n \leqslant b$ for all n.

In this case the numbers u_n move steadily to the right, but none of them will go beyond m. We, therefore, assume the theorem as an *axiom* which states in the circumstances mentioned above that there is some number b towards which u_n converges as $n \to \infty$. This is known as the *axiom of continuity*.

Theorem 3: If $|r| < 1$, then $r^n \to 0$ as $n \to \infty$. If r is positive and less than 1,

r^2, r^3, r^4, ... go on decreasing. For instance, if $r = \frac{7}{8}$, $(\frac{7}{8})^2 < \frac{7}{8}$, as $\frac{7}{8} \cdot \frac{7}{8} < \frac{7}{8} \cdot 1$
$(\frac{7}{8})^3 < (\frac{7}{8})^2$ as $(\frac{7}{8})^2 \cdot \frac{7}{8} < (\frac{7}{8})^2 \cdot 1$ and so on.

If $\epsilon = \frac{1}{100}$ we can find N such that $r^n < \epsilon$ for all $n > N$. Here $(\frac{7}{8})^n < \frac{1}{100}$ or $(\frac{8}{7})^n > 100$ for all $n > N$, to be found. Taking the logarithms

$n(\log 8 - \log 7) > 2$ i.e.

$n(\cdot 9031 - \cdot 8451) > 2$ (from the four place logarithm tables)

$\therefore n > \dfrac{2}{\cdot 058}$ or $n > \frac{2000}{58}$

i.e. $n > \frac{1000}{29}$ or $n > 37$ $\therefore N = 37$

$\therefore r^n < \frac{1}{100}$ for $n > 37$.

Similarly if $r = -\frac{7}{8}$, $r^n < \pm \frac{1}{100}$ for all $n > 37$.

$\therefore r^n \to 0$ as $n \to \infty$.

Theorem 4: If $u_n = c$ for every n,

then $\lim\limits_{n \to \infty} u_n = c$, where c any constant.

This is easily seen to be true as $u_n = c$ whatever be the value of n as $c - \epsilon \leqslant u_n \leqslant c + \epsilon$ for a given ϵ.

Theorem 5: If $|u_n| \geqslant n\,c$ where c is any positive constant, then the sequence $|u_1|$, $|u_2|$, $|u_3|$, ... $|u_n|$ diverges.

$u_{n+1}|$ can be made greater than any given large number, say 10000.

Since $|u_n| \geqslant nc$,

for all $n > \dfrac{10000}{c}$, $|u_n| > 10000$.

Hence $|u_n| \to \infty$ as $n \to \infty$.

10.5. A sequence is said to be monotonic increasing if its elements are always increasing i.e. if $u_{n+1} > u_n$ for all n. If $u_n > u_{n+1}$, the sequence is said to be monotonic decreasing.

For example, 1, $\frac{1}{2}$, $\frac{1}{3}$, ..., $\dfrac{1}{n}$ is a monotonic decreasing sequence, as $\dfrac{1}{n} > \dfrac{1}{n+1}$ for all n.

The sequence $\frac{1}{2}$, $\frac{2}{3}$, $\frac{3}{4}$, $\frac{4}{5}$, ... is a monotonic increasing sequence, as $\dfrac{n+1}{n+2} > \dfrac{n}{n+1}$, for

$(n+1)^2 - n(n+2) = 1 > 0$

Theorem 6: A monotonic sequence always tends to a limit. (finite or infinite). That is, a monotonic sequence either converges or tends to $\pm\infty$.

Consider a monotonic increasing sequence. If its upper bound M is finite, $u_n \leqslant M$ for all n and there is at least one u_n such that $u_n > M - \epsilon$. [See section 10·2]

Since the sequence is monotonic increasing,

$u_{n+1} > u_n > M - \epsilon$, and $u_n > M - \epsilon$ for all $n > N$ (N depending on ϵ).

∴ $M - \epsilon < u_n \leqslant M$ for all $n > N$.

Since ϵ can be taken as small as we like,

$u_n \to M$ as $n \to \infty$.

If M is infinite, we can find N for any given positive number L, however large it may be, such that

$u_n > L$ for all $n \geqslant N$.

∴ $u_n \to \infty$ as $n \to \infty$.

Similarly a decreasing monotonic sequence $\to a$ finite limit or $-\infty$, as $n \to \infty$.

The following theorem on a monotonic sequence is important.

Theorem 7 : The sequence $u_n = \left(1 + \dfrac{1}{n}\right)^n$ where n is a positive integer, tends to a limit as $n \to \infty$.

By Binomial theorem for a positive integer,

$$\left(1 + \frac{1}{n}\right)^n = 1 n \cdot \frac{1}{n} + \frac{n(n-1)}{2!} \cdot \frac{1}{n^2} + \frac{n(n-1)(n-2)}{3!} \cdot \frac{1}{n^3} + \ldots$$

to $n+1$ terms.

$$= 1 + 1 + \frac{1}{2!}\left(1 - \frac{1}{n}\right) + \frac{1}{3!}\left(1 - \frac{1}{n}\right)\left(1 - \frac{2}{n}\right) + \ldots \ldots (1)$$

Now in this series, every term is positive and increases with n, as terms like $\dfrac{1}{n}$, $\dfrac{2}{n}$ go on decreasing with n; also, the number of terms increases with n. Hence u_n is monotonic increasing.

Again as $\left(1-\dfrac{1}{n}\right)$, $\left(1-\dfrac{2}{n}\right)$ ...... are positive and each less than 1, we have from (1)

$$\left(1+\frac{1}{n}\right)^n < 1+1+\frac{1}{2!}+\frac{1}{3!}+\frac{1}{4!} \cdots \cdots +\frac{1}{n!}$$

Now $\dfrac{1}{r!} = \dfrac{1}{1 \cdot 2 \cdot 3 \cdot 4 \dots r} < \dfrac{1}{1 \cdot 2 \cdot 2 \cdot 2 \dots 2}$

$\therefore \dfrac{1}{r!} < \dfrac{1}{2^{r-1}}$ for all integral values of $r \geqslant 3$.

$$\therefore \left(1+\frac{1}{n}\right)^n < 1+1+\tfrac{1}{2}+\frac{1}{2^2}+\frac{1}{2^3}+ \cdots \cdots +\frac{1}{2^{n-1}}$$

$$=1+2\left(1-\frac{1}{2^n}\right)=3-\frac{1}{2^{n-1}}$$

$$\therefore \left(1+\frac{1}{n}\right)^n < 3 \text{ for all } n.$$

Now from the above theorem, $\left(1+\dfrac{1}{n}\right)^n$ which is monotonic increasing, must tend to a finite limit or ∞. Since it is less than 3, it cannot tend to ∞.

$$\therefore \left(1+\frac{1}{n}\right)^n \to \text{ a definite limit } < 3.$$

From (1) above, the limit > 2.

$$\therefore \lim_{n \longrightarrow \infty} \left(1+\frac{1}{n}\right)^n = l > 2 \text{ but } < 3.$$

The value of l is approximately $2 \cdot 7$. We denote it by e, which is used as a base for natural logarithms.

10.6. An infinite series.

An expression such as

$u_1+u_2+u_3+ \dots +u_{93}$ is called a finite series. The sum of such a series can be found by adding all the 93 terms with some trouble. Now we consider an expression of the form $u_1+u_2 + \ldots\ldots +u_n + \ldots\ldots$ This series is unending and there is always a term u_n, however great the integer n be. We have first to find a meaning for such an infinite number of additions. We do this by finding partial sums:

$s_1=u_1,\; s_2=u_1+u_2,\; s_3=u_1+u_2+u_3 \ldots.$

$s_k=u_1+u_2 + \ldots\ldots +u_k.$ Each partial sum is obtained simply by a finite number of additions.

Definition : Given the infinite series $u_1+u_2+ \ldots. +u_n+ \ldots\ldots,$ we define its sum as $\lim\limits_{n \to -\infty} s_n$, where $s_n=u_1+u_2+ \ldots. +u_n.$

Of course, we are not sure that a finite limit exists. If such a limit exists, the series $u_1+u_2+ \ldots. +u_n +\ldots.$ is said to *converge* to that limit. If there is no finite limit, the series is said to *diverge*.

The simplest example of a divergent series is $1+2+3 + \ldots\ldots +n + \ldots\ldots$ Here $s_n = \dfrac{n(n+1)}{2}$ and has no finite limit as $n \to \infty$. Here s_n contains the terms $\frac{1}{2}n^2$ and $\frac{1}{2}n$ each of which becomes larger and larger as n increases. On the other hand, consider the series of geometric progression

$$1+\tfrac{1}{2}+\frac{1}{2^2} + \ldots\ldots + \frac{1}{2^{n-1}} + \ldots\ldots$$

Here $s_n=2\left(1-\dfrac{1}{2^n}\right)=2-\dfrac{1}{2^{n-1}}.$

Now $\dfrac{1}{2^{n-1}}$ can be made as small as we please [see ex. *b* of 10·2 above].

$\therefore$ the limit $\lim\limits_{n \to \infty} s_n=2.$ You are already familiar with the geometric series, the general theorem on which may be stated as under:

A geometric series

$$a + ar + ar^2 + \ldots\ldots + ar^{n-1} + \ldots.$$

converges if $-1 < r < 1$ and diverges if $|r| \geqslant 1$. The sum of the infinite series in the former case is $\dfrac{a}{1-r}$ where r is the common ratio.

$$s_n = \frac{a(1-r^n)}{1-r} = \frac{1}{1-r} - \frac{a\, r^n}{1-r}.$$

Now r^n tends to the limit 0 if $|r| < 1$, $r^n \to \infty$ if $|r| > 1$. If $r=1$, the partial sum $s_n = na$ which does not tend to a finite limit as $n \to \infty$. If $r=-1$, $s_n = 0$ if n is even and a if n is odd. Hence there is no finite limit if $r = \pm 1$. The series diverges if $|r| \geqslant 1$.

Theorem: The necessary condition for an infinite series $u_1 + u_2 + \ldots + \ldots + u_n + \ldots$ to be convergent is that $u_n \to 0$ as $n \to \infty$.

Writing $s_n = u_1 + u_2 + \ldots + u_n$ and $s_{n-1} = u_1 + u_2 + \ldots + u_{n-1}$, $u_n = s_n - s_{n-1}$. By theorem 1 (b) on limits,

$$\lim_{n \to \infty} u_n = \lim_{n \to \infty} s_n - \lim_{n \to \infty} s_{n-1}$$

If l is the limit of s, l is also the limit of s_{n-1} as $n \to \infty$; for by definition $l - \epsilon < s_n < l + \epsilon$ for all $n > N$ for a given ϵ. By taking n sufficiently large, we can make

$$l - \epsilon < s_{n-1} < l + \epsilon.$$

$\therefore \lim u_n = l - l = 0$. This is a necessary condition. The converse of this is not necessarily true. We shall come across some series which are not convergent although $u_n \to 0$, as $n \to \infty$. For instance, the series $1 + \frac{1}{2} + \frac{1}{3} + \ldots\ldots + \dfrac{1}{u}$

$+ \ldots\ldots$ will be proved to be divergent although $\dfrac{1}{n} \to 0$.

Corollary: If u_n does not tend to zero as $n \to \infty$, then the series $u_1 + u_2 + \ldots\ldots + u_n + \ldots\ldots$ is divergent.

Proof: If it is not divergent, it converges and $u_n \to 0$.

Summary of these discussions:

(1) The set of numbers u_1, u_2, u_3, u_4, $\ldots\ldots$ u_n forms a sequence. It is a function of n and if it is unending, it forms an infinite sequence.

(2) The limit of u_n is l when n tends to infinity, if given ϵ, there is a positive integer N such that $|u_n - l| < \epsilon$ for all $n \geqslant N$.

(3) A series $u_1 + u_2 + \ldots\ldots + u_n + \ldots\ldots$ *converges* if $s_n \to a$ limit as $n \to \infty$, where $s_n = \sum\limits_{n=1}^{n} u_n$.

Otherwise, the series is said to *diverge*.

(4) A necessary condition for the convergence of an infinite series $u_1 + u_2 + \ldots + u_n + \ldots$ is that $u_n \to 0$ as $n \to \infty$.

Illustrative examples.

1. The sequence 2, $\frac{3}{2}$, $\frac{4}{3}$, $\frac{5}{4}$, $\ldots$ tends to 1, as $n \to \infty$.

Here $f(n) = \dfrac{n+1}{n} = 1 + \dfrac{1}{n}$.

$$\lim_{n \to \infty} f(n) = \lim_{n \to \infty} 1 + \lim_{n \to \infty} \frac{1}{n}$$

$$= 1 + 0 \quad \because \frac{1}{n} \to 0 \text{ as } n \to \infty$$

$$= 1.$$

From first principles we can find N for a given ϵ, such that $\left| \dfrac{n+1}{n} - 1 \right| < \epsilon$ for all $n \geqslant N$.

If $\epsilon = \frac{1}{1000}$

$$\left| \frac{n+1}{n} - 1 \right| = \frac{1}{n} < \frac{1}{1000} \text{ for all } n > 1001.$$

Example 2: The sequences $\sqrt{1}, \sqrt{2}, \sqrt{3}, \ldots \ldots \sqrt{n}$, tends to infinity as n tends to infinity.

Here u_n or $f(n)$ is $\sqrt{n}$ and this can be made larger than N by giving n values $> N^2$.

If $N = (10)^6$, we can give n values $> (10)^{12}$ to make $\sqrt{n} > 10^6$. Hence $\sqrt{n}$ becomes larger than any preassigned number, however large it may be.

Example 3: Prove that the sequences $f(n) = \dfrac{2n+4}{7n+2}$ converges to the limit $\frac{2}{7}$.

$$f(n) = \frac{2n+4}{7n+2} = \frac{n\left(2+\dfrac{4}{n}\right)}{n\left(7+\dfrac{2}{n}\right)} = \frac{2+\dfrac{4}{n}}{7+\dfrac{2}{n}} \text{ as long as}$$

n is a specific number however large it may be.

$$\therefore f(n) = \frac{2+\dfrac{4}{n}}{7+\dfrac{2}{n}} \text{ and } \lim_{n\to\infty} f(n) = \frac{\lim\left(2+\dfrac{4}{n}\right)}{\lim\left(7+\dfrac{2}{n}\right)}$$

as $n \to \infty$ by theorem 1 (d) on limits.

Since $\dfrac{4}{n}$ and $\dfrac{2}{n} \to 0$, as $n \to \infty$

$$\lim_{n\to\infty} f(n) = \tfrac{2}{7}.$$

Example 4: The sequence is $u_1, u_2, u_3, \ldots$ where $u_n = \dfrac{1}{n^2} + \dfrac{2}{n^2} + \dfrac{3}{n^2} + \ldots \ldots + \dfrac{n}{n^2}$. Find the limit of u_n as $n \to \infty$.

$$u_n = f(n) = \frac{1}{n^2} (1+2+3+\ldots+n)$$

$$= \frac{1}{n^2} \cdot \frac{n(n+1)}{2}$$

$$= \frac{n+1}{2n}$$

$$= \tfrac{1}{2}\left(1 + \frac{1}{n}\right)$$

$$\lim u_n \quad = \lim\left(\frac{1}{2} + \frac{1}{n}\right) \text{ as } n \to \infty$$

$$= \tfrac{1}{2} + 0 \text{ as } \frac{1}{n} \to 0 \text{ as } n \to \infty.$$

Example 5: $u_n = 1 + (-1)^n$. Discuss whether it converges.
The sequence is 0, 2, 0,2,0, ...

∴ u_n is 2 if n is even and 0 if n is odd.   Hence at no stage can we make u_n as small as we please for all $n > N$.   For an odd n, u_n is 0 and for the next integer $n+1$, u_{n+1} will be 2.

∴ u_n does not converge.   It oscillates between 0 and 2.

Example 6: Find whether the following series is convergent and if so, find its sum.

$$\frac{1}{1 \cdot 2} + \frac{1}{2 \cdot 3} + \cdots\cdots + \frac{1}{n(n+1)} + \cdots\cdots$$

Notice that the nth term is $\dfrac{1}{n} - \dfrac{1}{n+1}$

$$\therefore s_n = \begin{array}{l} 1 - \tfrac{1}{2} \\ + \tfrac{1}{2} - \tfrac{1}{3} \\ + \tfrac{1}{3} - \tfrac{1}{4} \\ \cdots\cdots\cdots\cdots \\ + \dfrac{1}{n-1} - \dfrac{1}{n} \end{array}$$

$$\therefore s_n = 1 - \frac{1}{n}$$

$$\lim_{n \to \infty} s_n = 1 - 0$$

$$= 1 \text{ since } \frac{1}{n} \to 0 \text{ as } n \to \infty.$$

Example 7 : Find the value of the repeating decimal
·77777 ......

A repeating decimal is really an infinite series. For instance the given decimal ·7777 ......

$$= \tfrac{7}{10} + \tfrac{7}{100} + \tfrac{7}{1000} + \ldots\ldots$$

$$= \tfrac{7}{10} \left\{ 1 + \tfrac{1}{10} + \frac{1}{10^2} + \frac{1}{10^3} + \ldots\ldots \frac{1}{10^n} + \ldots\ldots \right\}$$

$$= \tfrac{7}{10} \cdot \frac{1}{1 - \tfrac{1}{10}} = \tfrac{7}{10} \cdot \tfrac{10}{9} = \tfrac{7}{9} \quad \text{as}$$

$1 + \tfrac{1}{10} + \ldots\ldots$ is a Geometric series with common ratio $\tfrac{1}{10}$.

Exercise 10·1

Determine which of the following sequences u_n converge and which of them diverge as $n \to \infty$. Find also the limit of the convergent sequences.

1. $u_n = \dfrac{n+1}{1-2n}$.

2. $u_n = \dfrac{n^2-3n}{2n^2+5n}$.

3. $u_n = 2 + \dfrac{(-1)^n}{n}$.

4. $u_n = 2 + (-\tfrac{1}{2})^n$.

5. $u_n = 1 + (-1)^n$.

6. $u_n = \dfrac{n^2+1}{2n^2-n+3}$.

7. $u_n = \dfrac{2^n-1}{2^n+1}$.

8. $u_n = \dfrac{n^2-n+5}{2n+3}$.

9. $u_n = \sin n\pi$.

10. $u_n = 2^{-n}$.

11. $u_n = 1 + \cos n\pi$.

12. $u_n = n \sin \dfrac{n\pi}{2}$.

13. $u_n = \sqrt{n+1} - \sqrt{n}$.

14. $u_n = \dfrac{x^n}{n!}$.

15. Find the least value of the integer n for which $\dfrac{n}{n^2+1}$ differs from its limit as $n \to \infty$, by less than 0·001.

16. Show that the series $\tfrac{1}{3} + \tfrac{1}{9} + \tfrac{1}{27} + \ldots\ldots$ converges to $\tfrac{1}{2}$.

17. Show that the series $3 - \frac{3}{2} + \frac{3}{4} - \frac{3}{8} + \ldots + \frac{(-1)^{n-1}3}{2^{n-1}} + \ldots$

converges to 2.

18. Show that the series $1 + \frac{3}{2} + \frac{9}{4} + \ldots + (\frac{3}{2})^{n-1} + \ldots$ diverges.

19. Show that the series $1 + 2^2 + 3^2 + \ldots + n^2 + \ldots$ diverges.

20. Show that $\dfrac{9}{100} + \dfrac{9}{(100)^2} + \dfrac{9}{(100)^3} + \ldots\ldots + \dfrac{9}{(100)^n} + \ldots$

converges to $\frac{1}{11}$.

21. Express $0 \cdot 35\ 35\ 35\ \ldots$ as a rational number.

22. Express $0 \cdot 123\ 123\ 123\ \ldots$ as a rational number.

23. Express $1 \cdot 357\ 357\ 357\ \ldots$ as a rational number.

24. A ball is dropped from a metre above a flat surface. Each time the ball hits the ground after falling a distance h metres, it rebounds a distance rh, where $0 < r < 1$. Find the total distance the ball travels.

10.7. Series of positive terms.

It is not always possible to find the partial sum s_n of an infinite series and its limit as n tends to infinity. Now we present some theorems which provide indirect tests for convergence or divergence. They apply to only positive (or non-negative) terms.

Theorem 1: If $u_1 + u_2 + \ldots\ldots u_n + \ldots$ and $v_1 + v_2 + \ldots\ldots + v_n + \ldots$ are two infinite series such that $v_n \leqslant u_n$ for all n and $\sum\limits_{n=1}^{\infty} u_n$ is known to be convergent then $\sum\limits_{n=1}^{\infty} v_n$ is convergent.

Proof: Let $s_n = u_1 + \ldots + u_n$ and $t_n = v_1 + v_2 + \ldots + v_n$. Then by hypothesis, $\lim\limits_{n \to \infty} s_n$ exists $= s$ (say). Since the terms are non-negative

$t_n \leqslant s_n \leqslant s$ for all values of n.   Also $t_n < t_{n+1} \leqslant s$ for all n.

Hence by theorem 2 of section 10·4,

$\quad$ lim t_n exists and $\leqslant$ s.

$\quad n \longrightarrow \infty$

Theorem 2: If $v_n \geqslant u_n$ for all n and the series $\overset{\infty}{\underset{1}{\Sigma}} u_n$ diverges, then the series Σv_n also diverges.

$\quad$ Here $t_n \geqslant s_n$ for all n.

$\quad$ By hypothesis Σu_n is divergent.

$\quad \therefore$ we can find $\mathcal{N}$ such that $s_n >$ any given number for all $n \geqslant \mathcal{N}$.

$\quad \therefore t_n \geqslant$ any given number however large it may be, for all $n \geqslant \mathcal{N}$.

$\quad \therefore t_n \to \infty$ as $n \to \infty$.

In applying these theorems, any finite number of terms at the beginning of the series may be omitted. They do not make any difference to the results.

Example 8: Test the convergence or divergence of the infinite series $\dfrac{1}{1} + \dfrac{1}{2!} + \dfrac{1}{3!} + \ldots + \dfrac{1}{n!} + \ldots$

Now $\dfrac{1}{n!} = \dfrac{1}{1 \cdot 2 \cdot 3 \ldots n}$. Since each factor except 1 and 2 in $n!$ is larger than 2, we have

$$n! \geqslant 2^{n-1} \text{ and } \frac{1}{n!} \leqslant \frac{1}{2^{n-1}} \text{ for all } n.$$

Now $\overset{\infty}{\underset{n=1}{\Sigma}} \dfrac{1}{2^{n-1}}$ is a geometric series with the common ratio $\frac{1}{2}$ and is, therefore, known to be convergent.

By comparison test, $\overset{\infty}{\underset{n=1}{\Sigma}} \dfrac{1}{n!}$ is convergent. The geometric series always comes in handy for comparison. In addition, the series $1 + \dfrac{1}{2^p} + \dfrac{1}{3^p} + \ldots + \dfrac{1}{n^p} + \ldots$ is often useful for comparison. It is known as p-series.

Theorem 3: The series $\sum_{n=1}^{\infty} \frac{1}{n^p}$, known as the p-series, is convergent if $p > 1$ and divergent if $p \leqslant 1$.

Proof: Case 1. $p > 1$.

The series $\frac{1}{1^p} + \frac{1}{2^p} + \frac{1}{3^p} + \ldots\ldots + \frac{1}{n^p} + \ldots$ can be grouped by taking $2^0, 2^1, 2^2, 2^3, 2^4, \ldots 2^k \ldots$ terms; i.e.

$$\left(\frac{1}{1^p}\right) + \left(\frac{1}{2^p} + \frac{1}{3^p}\right) + \left(\frac{1}{4^p} + \frac{1}{5^p} + \frac{1}{6^p} + \frac{1}{7^p}\right) + \left(\frac{1}{8^p} + \frac{1}{9^p} + \ldots \frac{1}{15^p}\right)$$
$$+ \ldots\ldots\ldots\ldots\ldots\ldots\ldots\ldots\ldots\ldots\ldots\ldots\ldots\ldots\ldots$$

Thus there will be 2^{k-1} terms in the kth group of terms.

Now $1 \leqslant 1$

$$\frac{1}{2^p} + \frac{1}{3^p} \leqslant \frac{1}{2^p} + \frac{1}{2^p} = \frac{1}{2^{p-1}}$$

$$\frac{1}{4^p} + \frac{1}{5^p} + \frac{1}{6^p} + \frac{1}{7^p} \leqslant \frac{1}{4^p} + \frac{1}{4^p} + \frac{1}{4^p} + \frac{1}{4^p} = \frac{4}{4^p} = \frac{1}{4^{p-1}}$$

$$= \left(\frac{1}{2^{p-1}}\right)^2$$

$$\frac{1}{8^p} + \frac{1}{9^p} + \frac{1}{10^p} + \frac{1}{11^p} + \frac{1}{12^p} + \frac{1}{13^p} + \frac{1}{14^p} + \frac{1}{15^p} \leqslant \frac{1}{8^p} + \frac{1}{8^p}$$

$$+ \frac{1}{8^p} + \frac{1}{8^p} + \frac{1}{8^p} + \frac{1}{8^p} + \frac{1}{8^p} + \frac{1}{8^p} = \frac{8}{8^p} = \frac{1}{8^{p-1}} = \left(\frac{1}{2^{p-1}}\right)^3$$

and so on.

The terms on the right form a geometric series viz.

$$1 + \frac{1}{2^{p-1}} + \left(\frac{1}{2^{p-1}}\right)^2 + \left(\frac{1}{2^{p-1}}\right)^3 + \ldots \text{ with the common}$$

ratio $\frac{1}{2^{p-1}} < 1$, since $p > 1$.

It is, therefore, convergent, and the sum of the infinite series

$$= \cfrac{1}{1 - \cfrac{1}{2^{p-1}}}$$

$$= \frac{2^{p-1}}{2^{p-1}-1} = s \text{ (say)}$$

Since the terms of p-series in groups are $\leqslant$ those of the geometric series, the p-series is convergent, by comparison test.

Case 2: $p=1$. The p-series in this case is the harmonic series $1+\frac{1}{2}+\frac{1}{3}+\frac{1}{4}+\ldots\ldots$

The proof is on the same lines as given above.

The series can be grouped as

$1+\frac{1}{2}+(\frac{1}{3}+\frac{1}{4})+(\frac{1}{5}+\frac{1}{6}+\frac{1}{7}+\frac{1}{8})+\ldots\ldots$

Now $1+\frac{1}{2} > 1$

$\frac{1}{3}+\frac{1}{4} > \frac{1}{4}+\frac{1}{4}=\frac{1}{2}$

$\frac{1}{5}+\frac{1}{6}+\frac{1}{7}+\frac{1}{8} > \frac{1}{8}+\frac{1}{8}+\frac{1}{8}+\frac{1}{8}=\frac{1}{2}$

$\frac{1}{9}+\frac{1}{10}+\ldots\ldots+\frac{1}{16} > \frac{1}{16}+\frac{1}{16}+\ldots\ldots+\frac{1}{16} = \frac{1}{2}$

and so on.

$$\therefore \ 1+\frac{1}{2}+\frac{1}{3}+\frac{1}{4}+\ldots\ldots+\frac{1}{n} > 1+\frac{1}{2}+\frac{1}{2}+\frac{1}{2}+\frac{1}{2}+\ldots\ldots$$

The series on the right side increases beyond any number, however large it may be. $\therefore$ it is divergent.

$\therefore$ the harmonic series $1+\frac{1}{2}+\frac{1}{3}+\frac{1}{4}+\ldots\ldots+\frac{1}{n}+\ldots\ldots$

is divergent.

Case 3: $p < 1$.

Since $p < 1$, $n^p \leqslant n$ $\therefore \frac{1}{n^p} \geqslant \frac{1}{n}$.

$\therefore$ by comparison test with the harmonic series $1+\frac{1}{2}+\frac{1}{3}+\ldots\ldots$, the p-series is divergent, if $p < 1$.

Example 9 : Test the convergence or divergence of the series.

$$1 + \tfrac{1}{4} + \tfrac{1}{7} + \tfrac{1}{10} + \ldots\ldots + \frac{1}{3n-2} + \ldots\ldots$$

$$\frac{1}{3n-2} = \frac{1}{3\left(n-\frac{2}{3}\right)} \geqslant \frac{1}{3n} \text{ for all } n \geqslant 1$$

$$\therefore \sum_{1}^{\infty} \frac{1}{3n-2} \geqslant \tfrac{1}{3} \sum_{1}^{\infty} \frac{1}{n}.$$

The series on the right side is the harmonic series which is divergent.

∴ the given series is divergent.

Exercise 10.2

Test the following series for convergence or divergence.

1. $1 + \dfrac{1}{\sqrt{2}} + \dfrac{1}{\sqrt{3}} + \ldots\ldots$

2. $1 + \dfrac{1}{2\sqrt{2}} + \dfrac{1}{3\sqrt{3}} + \ldots\ldots$

3. $2 + \dfrac{3}{2\sqrt{2}} + \dfrac{4}{3\sqrt{3}} + \ldots\ldots + \dfrac{n+1}{n\sqrt{n}} + \ldots\ldots$

4. $\dfrac{1}{1\cdot2} + \dfrac{1}{2\cdot2^2} + \dfrac{1}{3\cdot2^3} + \dfrac{1}{4\cdot2^4} + \ldots\ldots + \dfrac{1}{n\cdot2^n} + \ldots\ldots$

5. $\dfrac{1}{2^3} + \dfrac{2}{3^3} + \dfrac{3}{4^3} + \ldots\ldots + \dfrac{n-1}{n^3} + \ldots\ldots$

6. $\dfrac{1}{\sqrt{1\cdot2}} + \dfrac{1}{\sqrt{2\cdot3}} + \dfrac{1}{\sqrt{3\cdot4}} + \ldots\ldots + \dfrac{1}{\sqrt{n(n+1)}} + \ldots\ldots$

7. $\dfrac{2}{2+3} + \dfrac{2}{2^2+3} + \dfrac{2}{2^3+3} + \ldots\ldots + \dfrac{2}{2^n+3} + \ldots\ldots$

8. $\dfrac{1}{2^2} + \dfrac{2}{3^2} + \dfrac{3}{4^2} + \ldots\ldots + \dfrac{n-1}{n^2} + \ldots\ldots$

9. $1 + \dfrac{2!}{1\cdot3} + \dfrac{3!}{1\cdot3\cdot5} + \ldots\ldots + \dfrac{n!}{1\cdot3\cdot5\cdot7\ldots(2n-1)} + \ldots$

10. $\dfrac{1}{\sqrt{2}} + \dfrac{1}{\sqrt{5}} + \dfrac{1}{\sqrt{10}} + \dfrac{1}{\sqrt{17}} + \ldots\ldots + \dfrac{1}{\sqrt{n^2+1}} + \ldots\ldots$

11. $\dfrac{1}{1\cdot3} + \dfrac{1}{2\cdot3^2} + \dfrac{1}{3\cdot3^3} + \ldots\ldots \dfrac{1}{n\cdot3^n} + \ldots\ldots$

12. $\dfrac{1}{1+3} + \dfrac{1}{1+3^2} + \dfrac{1}{1+3^3} + \ldots\ldots + \dfrac{1}{1+3^n} + \ldots\ldots$

13. $\dfrac{1}{1-\frac{1}{2}} + \dfrac{1}{2-\frac{1}{3}} + \dfrac{1}{3-\frac{1}{4}} + \ldots\ldots + \dfrac{1}{n-\dfrac{1}{n+1}}$

14. $\dfrac{1}{1\cdot2} + \dfrac{1}{2\cdot3} + \dfrac{1}{3\cdot4} + \ldots\ldots + \dfrac{1}{n(n+1)} + \ldots\ldots$

15. $\dfrac{1}{\sqrt{2}} + \dfrac{1}{\sqrt{6}} + \dfrac{1}{\sqrt{12}} + \ldots\ldots + \dfrac{1}{\sqrt{n(n+1)}} + \ldots\ldots$

Write down the first three terms of the series whose nth term is given and test for convergence or divergence.

16. $\dfrac{n}{n+1}.$ **17.** $\dfrac{1}{(2n-1)!}.$

18. $\dfrac{1}{2^n+n}.$ **19.** $\dfrac{1}{(2n)!}.$

20. $\dfrac{1}{(n+1)(n+2)}.$ **21.** $\dfrac{2n+3}{n^2+3n+2}.$

22. $\dfrac{n^2+n}{2n^2+n+1}.$ **23.** $\dfrac{1}{n^2+1}.$

24. $\dfrac{\sqrt{n}}{n^2}.$ **25.** $\dfrac{n^p}{(n+1)^q}.$

10.8. So far we were concerned with the series of positive terms only. If all the terms of a series are negative we can take out the common factor -1 and deal with it as though it were a series of positive terms. Some times some terms may be positive and some may be negative. They have to be dealt with separately. In this section we establish three theorems which provide important tests for the convergence and divergence of series whose terms are not necessarily positive. A series $u_1 + u_2 + \ldots\ldots + u_n + \ldots\ldots$ with some positive terms and some negative terms is said to *converge absolutely* if the series

$$| u_1 | + | u_2 | + | u_3 | + \ldots\ldots + | u_n | + \ldots\ldots$$

of the absolute values of its terms converges.

Theorem 4: If $\sum_{n=1}^{\infty} | u_n |$ converges, then $\sum_{n=1}^{\infty} u_n$ converges.

Proof: Let $s_n = u_1 + u_2 + \ldots\ldots + u_n$ be the partial sum of the first n terms of the given series. Let v_n be the sum of the positive terms and w_n be the sum of the absolute values of the negative terms in s_n so that

$s_n = v_n - w_n.$

If $t_n = | u_1 | + | u_2 | + \ldots\ldots + | u_n |$, then

$$t_n = v_n + w_n.$$

By hypothesis $t_n \to a$ limit, say l. $\therefore t_n = v_n + w_n \leqslant l$
    as all the terms in v_n and w_n are positive.

$\therefore v_n \leqslant l$ and $w_n \leqslant l.$

By theorem 2 section 10·4, $v_n \to a$ limit l_1,
    and $w_n \to a$ limit l_2 as $n \to \infty$.

$\therefore \lim_{n \to \infty} s_n = \lim_{n \to \infty} (v_n - w_n) = l_1 - l_2$, by the theorem, $1(b)$
    on limits.

$\therefore s_n$ converges to a limit. $\therefore$ the given series is convergent.

Note that if the series of absolute values $\sum_{1}^{n} | u_n |$ is convergent, the series itself is convergent from the above theorem. But the converse is not true.

Definition: A series $\sum\limits_{n=1}^{\infty} u_n$ is said to be *absolutely convergent* if $\sum\limits_{n=1}^{\infty} |u_n|$ is convergent. If $\sum\limits_{n=1}^{\infty} u_n$ converges and $\sum\limits_{n=1}^{\infty} n$ 1 is divergent, then the series $\sum\limits_{n=1}^{\infty} u_n$ is said to be *conditionally* convergent. The series whose terms are alternately positive and negative is said to be *alternating* series. For instance $1-\frac{1}{2}+\frac{1}{3}-\frac{1}{4}+\frac{1}{5}- \ldots \ldots +(-1)^{n-1}\frac{1}{n}+ \ldots \ldots$ is an alternating series.

Theorem 5 : The alternating series $u_1-u_2+u_3-u_4+ \ldots$ $+(-1)^{n-1} u_n+ \ldots \ldots$ converges if (a) $\lim\limits_{n \to \infty} u_n=0$, and (b) $u_{n+1} \leqslant u_n$ for all n.

Here the terms $u_1, u_2, u_3, \ldots$ are all assumed to be positive.

If m is any integer, $2m$ is any even positive integer. Now the sum s_{2m} of the first $2m$ term of the given series $u_1-u_2+u_3 - \ldots \ldots$ can be written in two ways:

$$s_{2m} = (u_1-u_2)+(u_3-u_4)+ \ldots (u_{2m-1}-u_{2m}) \ldots (1)$$
$$\text{and} \quad s_{2m} = u_1-(u_2-u_3)-(u_4-u_5)-(u_6-u_7) \ldots \ldots$$
$$-(u_{2m-2}-u_{2m-1})-u_{2m} \quad \ldots \ldots (2)$$

Since each term is less than or equal to its predecessor by hypothesis, each bracketed portion of the series (1) and (2) is positive. (1) implies that s_{2m} increases while (2) implies that $s_{2m} < u_1$ for all m. By theorem 2, section 10·4, s_{2m} tends to a limit s as $m \to \infty$.

Let s_{2m+1} be the sum of an odd number of terms. Then $s_{2m+1} = s_{2m}+u_{2m+1}.$

$$\therefore \lim_{m \to \infty} s_{2m+1} = \lim_{m \to \infty} s_{2m} + \lim_{m \to \infty} u_{2m+1}$$

$$= s + 0 \text{ (as proved already)}$$

$$= s$$

$\therefore s_n \to s$ whether n is odd or even.

Corollary: $|s - s_n| \leqslant |u_{n+1}|$; for

$$|s - s_n| = |u_{n+1} - (u_{n+2} - u_{n+3}) - (u_{n+4} - u_{n+5}) - \ldots \ldots |$$
$$\leqslant u_{n+1}.$$

Example 10: Show that $1 - \frac{1}{2} + \frac{1}{3} - \frac{1}{4} + \ldots \ldots$ is convergent.

Here $u_n = \dfrac{1}{n} \to 0$ as $n \to \infty$.

Also $\dfrac{1}{n+1} < \dfrac{1}{n}$ for all n.

The conditions of theorem 5 are satisfied and the series is convergent.

10.9. The ratio tests.

Suppose that in the series $u_1 + u_2 + \ldots \ldots + u_n \ldots \ldots$, every $u_n \neq 0$ and that $\lim\limits_{n \to \infty} \left| \dfrac{u_{n+1}}{u_n} \right|$ exists and $= R$.

Theorem 16: If $R < 1$, the series converges absolutely, if $R > 1$ the series diverges and if $R = 1$, the test fails to decide whether or not the series converges.

Proof: (i) If $R < 1$, choose any r such that $R < r < 1$.

Since $\lim\limits_{n \to \infty} \left| \dfrac{u_{n+1}}{u_n} \right| = R$, there must be a sufficiently large

N such that $\left| \dfrac{u_{n+1}}{u_n} \right| < r$ for all $n \geqslant N$.

For, if $r - R = \in$ we can make $\left| \dfrac{u_{n+1}}{u_n} \right| - R < \epsilon$ for all $n \geqslant N$.

Now $\left| \dfrac{u_{n+1}}{u_n} \right| = \dfrac{|u_{n+1}|}{|u_n|}$ so that $|u_{n+1}| < r\,|u_n|$,

$|u_{n+2}| < r\,|u_{n+1}|$, $|u_{n+3}| < r\,|u_{n+2}|$ for all $n \geqslant N$.

By substituting we find $|u_{N+1}| < r\,|u_N|$, $|u_{N+2}| < r\,|u_{N+1}|$ $< r^2\,|u_N|$, $|u_{N+3}| < r\,|u_{N+2}| < r^2\,|u_{N+1}| < r^3\,|u_N|$ etc.

and, in general, $|u_{N+k}| < r^k\,|u_N|$.

Now the series $|u_N| + |u_{N+1}| + |u_{N+2}| + |u_{N+3}| + \ldots\ldots$

$+ |u_{N+k}| + \ldots < |u_N|\,\{1 + r + r^2 + \ldots\}$

Since $r < 1$, this geometric series is convergent.

$\therefore\ |u_N| + |u_{N+1}| + |u_{N+2}| + \ldots + |u_{N+k}| + \ldots$

is convergent.

But the difference between this series and the series

$u_1| + |u_2| + |u_3| \ldots\ldots + |u_N| + |u_{N+1}| + \ldots$ is only a finite number of terms ($N-1$ to be exact).

$\therefore\ |u_1| + |u_2| + \ldots + |u_n| + \ldots\ldots$ is convergent.

(ii) Suppose that $R > 1$

Then there is an N for a given ϵ such that $\left| \dfrac{u_{n+1}}{u_n} \right| > R - \epsilon > 1$ for all $n \geqslant N$ by the definition of a limit.

$\therefore\ |u_{n+1}| > |u_n|$ for all $n \geqslant N$.

$\therefore\ \lim\limits_{n \to \infty} |u_n| \neq 0$. $\therefore$ the necessary condition for the convergence is not satisfied.

$\therefore$ the series diverges.

(iii) **In** case R$=1$, the test fails. Now we know that

$1 + \dfrac{1}{2^p} + \dfrac{1}{3^p} + \ldots\ldots$ is convergent when $p > 1$

and divergent when $p = 1$ by the p-series; but applying the **ratio** test,

$$\frac{1}{(n+1)^p} \div \frac{1}{n^p} = \left(\frac{n}{n+1}\right)^p = \left(\frac{1}{1+\frac{1}{n}}\right)^p$$

$$\to 1 \text{ as } n \to \infty. \quad \therefore R = 1.$$

This gives no information about the convergence or divergence. So we cannot find out the nature of the series by this method.

Note: In the case of positive terms $\left|\frac{u_{n+1}}{u_n}\right|$ becomes $\frac{u_{n+1}}{u_n}$ and we can apply the ratio test to $\frac{u_{n+1}}{u_n}$. A good working procedure for a student is to try first the ratio test. If the limit of $\left|\frac{u_{n+1}}{u_n}\right| > 1$, the series is divergent and if the limit < 1, the series is convergent. We try some other tests when the limit $= 1$.

Example 11: Test for the convergence of $\frac{1}{2} + \frac{2^2}{2!} + \frac{2^3}{3!} + \cdots$

$$\frac{u_{n+1}}{u_n} = \frac{2^{n+1}}{n+1!} \times \frac{n!}{2^n} = \frac{2}{n+1} \to 0 \text{ as } n \to \infty$$

$$\therefore \lim_{n \to \infty} \frac{u_{n+1}}{u_n} = 0 \quad \therefore \text{ the series is convergent.}$$

Example 12: Test for the convergence or the divergence of the series.

$$\tfrac{1}{2} - \tfrac{2}{3} + \tfrac{3}{4} - \cdots + \frac{(-1)^{n+1}n}{n+1} + \cdots$$

Theorem 5 above on alternating series is not applicable here as the absolute value of each term is greater than the preceding one. Now we try the ratio test.

$$\left| \frac{u_{n+1}}{u_n} \right| = \frac{n+1}{n+2} \times \frac{n+1}{n} = \frac{(n+1)^2}{n(n+2)}$$

$$= \frac{n^2+2n+1}{n^2+2n} = \frac{1+\dfrac{2}{n}+\dfrac{1}{n^2}}{1+\dfrac{2}{n}}$$

$$\therefore \lim_{n \to \infty} \left| \frac{u_{n+1}}{u_n} \right| = 1$$

This test also fails. We, therefore, try some other method.

$$u_1 = 1-\tfrac{1}{2},\ u_2 = 1-\tfrac{1}{3},\ u_3 = 1-\tfrac{1}{4}$$

$$\therefore s_{2n} = u_1 - u_2 + u_3 - u_4 + \dots + u_{2n-1} - u_{2n}$$

$$= (1-\tfrac{1}{2}) - (1-\tfrac{1}{3}) + (1-\tfrac{1}{4}) - (1-\tfrac{1}{5}) + \dots - (1-\tfrac{1}{2n})$$

$$= \left(\frac{1}{2} - \frac{1}{3} + \frac{1}{4} - \dots + \frac{1}{2}n \right) \to \log 2 - 1 \text{ as } n \to \infty.$$

Similarly $s_{2n+1} = \left(1 - \dfrac{1}{2} + \dfrac{1}{3} - \dots + \dfrac{1}{2n+1} \right) \to \log 2$

$\therefore$ the series does not tend to a definite limit. Here it actually oscillates finitely.

Exercise 10.3

Discuss the convergence or divergence of the following series:

1. $1 - \dfrac{1}{3} + \dfrac{1}{5} - \dfrac{1}{7} + \dfrac{1}{9} - \dots \dfrac{(-1)^{n-1}}{2n-1} + \dots$

2. $1 - \dfrac{1}{2} + \dfrac{1}{2^2} - \dfrac{1}{2^3} + \dots + \dfrac{(-1)^{n+1}n}{2^n} - \dots$

3. $\dfrac{1!}{10} + \dfrac{2!}{10^2} + \dfrac{3!}{10^3} + \dots + \dfrac{n!}{10^n} + \dots$

4. $1 + \dfrac{1}{3} + \dfrac{1}{5} + \dfrac{1}{7} + \dots$

5. $\dfrac{1}{3!} + \dfrac{1}{4!} + \dots + \dfrac{1}{n!} + \dots$

6. $\dfrac{2}{1!} + \dfrac{2^2}{2!} + \dfrac{2^3}{3!} + \dots + \dfrac{2^n}{n!} + \dots$

7. $3 + \dfrac{9}{2} + \dfrac{27}{3} + \ldots\ldots + \dfrac{3^n}{n} + \ldots\ldots$

8. $\dfrac{1}{2} + \dfrac{2}{2^2} + \dfrac{3}{2^3} + \ldots\ldots + \dfrac{n}{2^n} + \ldots\ldots$

9. $1 - \dfrac{1}{\sqrt{2}} + \dfrac{1}{\sqrt{3}} - \dfrac{1}{\sqrt{4}} + \ldots\ldots + \dfrac{(-1)^{n+1}}{\sqrt{n}} + \ldots\ldots$

10. $1 - \dfrac{1}{3!} + \dfrac{1}{5!} - \ldots\ldots + \dfrac{(-1)^{n+1}}{(2n-1)!} + \ldots\ldots$

11. $-1 + \dfrac{1}{2^{3/2}} - \dfrac{1}{3^{3/2}} + \dfrac{1}{4^{3/2}} - \ldots\ldots + \dfrac{(-1)^n}{n^{3/2}} + \ldots$

12. $\dfrac{1}{2} - \dfrac{1}{3} + \dfrac{1}{4} - \ldots\ldots + \dfrac{(-1)^{n+1}}{n+1} + \ldots\ldots$

Prove that

13. $\displaystyle\sum_{n=1}^{\infty} \dfrac{1}{(2n^2+1)!}$ converges.

14. $\displaystyle\sum_{n=1}^{\infty} \dfrac{1}{3^n n^2}$ converges.

15. $\displaystyle\sum_{n=1}^{\infty} \dfrac{2^n\, n!}{n^n}$ converges.

16. $\displaystyle\sum_{n=1}^{\infty} \dfrac{3^n\, n!}{n^n}$ diverges.

17. $\displaystyle\sum_{n=1}^{\infty} \dfrac{1 \cdot 3 \ldots\ldots (2n-1)}{3^n \cdot n!}$ converges.

18. $\displaystyle\sum_{n=1}^{\infty} \dfrac{3^n}{n!}$ converges.

19. $\displaystyle\sum_{n=1}^{\infty} \dfrac{2^n}{n^2}$ diverges.

20. $\displaystyle\sum_{n=1}^{\infty} \dfrac{1}{2n^2}$ converges.

21. $\displaystyle\sum_{n=1}^{\infty} \dfrac{(2n)!}{n^{100}}$ diverges.

22. $\sum\limits_{n=1}^{\infty} \dfrac{n!}{n^n}$ converges.

23. $\sum\limits_{n=1}^{\infty} \dfrac{(-2)^{n-1}}{n \cdot n!}$ is absolutely convergent.

24. $\sum\limits_{n=1}^{\infty} \dfrac{(-1)^{n-1} 5^n}{3^n \, n^2}$ diverges.

25. $\sum\limits_{n=1}^{\infty} \dfrac{n^2}{2^n}$ converges.

26. $\sum\limits_{n=1}^{\infty} \dfrac{2^n}{n^3+1}$ diverges.

27. $\sum\limits_{n=1}^{\infty} \dfrac{(-1)^{n-1} 10^n}{n!}$ absolutely converges.

CHAPTER 11

Power Series

11.1. If a_0, a_1, a_2 .... a_n, ... are constants, then the series $a_0 + a_1 x + a_2 x^2 + ... + a_n x^n + ...$ is called a *power series*. In the preceding chapter, we were concerned with the convergence or divergence of the series whose terms were constants. The characteristic of a power series is that each term has a power of x as well as a constant. The general term is $a_n x^n$ and the power series is often written $\sum\limits_{n=0}^{\infty} a_n x^n$. Ordinarily we use the ratio test to determine the value of x for which a power series converges. These values of x are generally within a certain internal $-r < x < r$, r having any value between 0 and ∞. This interval is spoken of as the *region of convergence*. It automatically includes $x=0$, as the series is obviously convergent and is equal to a_0 when $x=0$.

For example, consider the geometric series $\sum\limits_{n=0}^{\infty} x^n$. Applying the ratio test, $\lim\limits_{n \to \infty} \left| \dfrac{u_{n+1}^u}{u_n} \right| = \left| \dfrac{x^n}{x^{n-1}} \right| = | x |$.

∴ the series converges absolutely if $| x | < 1$ and diverges if $x | > 1$. The test fails when $| x | = 1$.

If $x=1$, the series becomes $1+1+1+1+ ......$ and is divergent as $s_n = n \to \infty$.

If $x = -1$, the series becomes

$1 - 1 + 1 - 1 + 1 - 1 + ...$

∴ $s_n = 1$ or 0 according as n is odd or even.

∴ the series is not convergent, as the limit oscillates between 0 and 1.

∴ the interval of convergence is $-1 < x < 1$. Thus the geometric series $1+x+x^2+ \ldots$ is convergent in that interval, and $= \dfrac{1}{1-x}$ provided x lies in the interval $-1 < x < 1$. It is not equal to $\dfrac{1}{1-x}$ for the values $+1$ and -1 of x.

11.2. *Theorem* 1: If a power series $\sum\limits_{n=0}^{\infty} a_n x^n$ is convergent for $x=k(k \neq 0)$, then it converges absolutely for all $|x| < |k|$. If the series diverges for $x=d$, then it diverges for all $|x| > |d|$.

Proof: Let $\sum\limits_{n=0}^{\infty} a_n x^n$ be convergent for $x=k$. The necessary condition of convergence of a series is that $u_n \to 0$ as $n \to \infty$

∴ $a_n k^n \to 0$ as $n \to \infty$.

For a given ϵ, we can find an N such that for all values of $n \geqslant N$, $|a_n k^n| < \epsilon$. Take $\epsilon = 1$.

∴ $|a_n k^n| < 1$ or $|a_n| < \left|\dfrac{1}{k}\right|^n$ for $n \geqslant N$.

Now take any x such that $|x| < k$ and consider

$|a_0| + |a_1 x| + \ldots + |a_N x^N| + |a_{N+1} x^{N+1}| + \ldots$

Since in dealing with an infinite series, we can ignore a finite number of terms, we may ignore here the first N terms.

Now $a_N x^N + a_{N+1} x^{N+1} + \ldots$

$< \left|\dfrac{x}{k}\right|^N + \left|\dfrac{x}{k}\right|^{N+1} + \ldots$

as $|a_n| < \dfrac{1}{|k^n|}$ for all $n \geqslant N$.

The series on the right side of this inequality is a geometric series which is absolutely convergent for $\left|\dfrac{x}{k}\right| < 1$.

$\therefore$ for $|x| < k$, by comparison test, $\displaystyle\sum_{n=0}^{\infty} a_n x^n$ converges absolutely. This proves the first half of the theorem.

For the second half, if the result is not true, let us assume that for a certain value X of x such that $|X| > |d|$, the series converges. If we take $k=X$, by the first half of the theorem, the series converges absolutely for all $|x| < |X|$. Now $|d| < |X|$. $\therefore$ the series converges absolutely for $x=d$. This is contrary to the hypothesis.

$\therefore$ if the series diverges for $x=d$, it diverges for all $|x| > |d|$.

As a result of this theorem, a power series behaves in one of the following ways:—

(a) It may converge only for $x=0$.

(b) It may converge absolutely for all finite x such that $-\infty < x < \infty$.

(c) There may be a positive number r such that the series converges absolutely for $|x| < r$ and diverges for $|x| > r$. When $|x| = r$ it may converge or diverge. Each case has to be dealt with separately.

Example 1 : Find the values of x for which the series $\displaystyle\sum_{n=1}^{\infty} \frac{1}{n} x^n$ converges.

Applying the ratio test

$$\lim_{n \to \infty} \left| \frac{\dfrac{1}{n+1} x^{n+1}}{\dfrac{1}{n} x^n} \right| = \lim_{n \to \infty} \left| \frac{n}{n+1} x \right| = \lim_{n \to \infty} \left| \frac{n}{n+1} \right| \cdot \lim |x|$$

$$= 1 \cdot \lim |x|$$

$\therefore r = |x|$.

$\therefore$ the series converges absolutely if $|x| < 1$, diverges if $|x| > 1$.

When $x=1$, the series becomes

$1+\frac{1}{2}+\frac{1}{3}+ \ldots \ldots$ which is known to be divergent.

If $x=-1$, the series will be

$$1-\frac{1}{2}+\frac{1}{3}-\frac{1}{4}+ \ldots \ldots$$

This series is convergent by the alternating series theorem.

$\therefore$ the interval of convergence is $-1 \leqslant x < 1$.

Example 2: Find the interval of convergence of series

$$1+\frac{x}{1}+\frac{x^2}{1+2}+\frac{x^3}{1+2+3}+ \ldots \ldots$$

Here for $n>1$, $u_{n+1} = \dfrac{x^n}{1+2+3+\ldots +n} = \dfrac{x^n \cdot 2}{n(n+1)}$ and

$$u_n = \frac{2x^{n-1}}{n(n-1)}$$

Applying ratio test we have

$$\left| \frac{u_{n+1}}{u_n} \right| = \left| \frac{2x^n}{n(n+1)} \cdot \frac{n(n-1)}{2x^{n-1}} \right|$$

$$= \frac{n-1}{n+1} \cdot |x|$$

$\therefore \lim\limits_{n \to \infty} \left| \dfrac{u_{n+1}}{u_n} \right| = |x|$ as $\dfrac{n-1}{n+1} = \dfrac{1-\dfrac{1}{n}}{1+\dfrac{1}{n}} \to 1$ as $n \to \infty$.

$\therefore \Sigma u_n$ is convergent if $x < 1$ and divergent if $x > 1$.

Also $1+2+3+ \ldots +n = \dfrac{n(n+1)}{2} > \dfrac{n^2}{2}$

$\therefore \dfrac{1}{1+2+\ldots +n} < \dfrac{2}{n^2}$

$\therefore$ when $x=1$, the series is less than $1+\dfrac{2}{1}+\dfrac{2}{2^2}+\dfrac{2}{3^2}+\ldots$

From the p-series, we know $\Sigma \dfrac{1}{n^2}$ is convergent. $\therefore$ the given series is convergent when $x = 1$.

If $x = -1$, the series will be $1 - \frac{1}{2} + \dfrac{1}{1+2} - \dfrac{1}{1+2+3} + \cdots$ which is convergent by the alternating series theorem.

$\therefore$ the interval of convergence is $-1 \leqslant x \leqslant 1$.

Example 3: Find the interval of convergence of the series $\dfrac{(x+2)}{2 \cdot 1^1} - \dfrac{(x+2)^3}{2^2 \cdot 2^2} + \dfrac{(x+2)^3}{2^3 \cdot 3^2} - \cdots$

The series here is in powers of $(x+2)$ instead of in x. It does not make any difference. The treatment is just the same.

Here $u_n = \dfrac{(-1)^{n-1}(x+2)^n}{2^n \quad n^2}$ and $u_{n+1} = \dfrac{(-1)^n(x+2)^{n+1}}{2^{n+1}(n+1)^2}$

$\therefore \left| \dfrac{u_{n+1}}{u_n} \right| = \left| \dfrac{-(x+2)^{n+1}}{2^{n+1}(n+1)^2} \cdot \dfrac{2^n \; n^2}{(x+2)^n} \right|$

$\qquad = \tfrac{1}{2} \cdot \left| x+2 \right| \cdot \left(\dfrac{n}{n+1} \right)^2$

$\lim_{n \to \infty} \left(\dfrac{n}{n+1} \right)^2 = \lim_{n \to \infty} \left(\dfrac{n}{n+1} \right) \cdot \lim_{n \to \infty} \left(\dfrac{n}{n+1} \right)$

$\qquad = 1 \cdot 1 = 1$

$\therefore r = \tfrac{1}{2} \left| x+2 \right|$.

The series is convergent if $\left| x+2 \right| < 2$ and divergent if $\left| x+2 \right| > 2$.

Now $\left| x+2 \right| < 2$ may be written
$\qquad -2 < x+2 < 2 \quad \text{or} \quad -4 < x < 0.$

At the end points of the interval, the series are

$$\sum \frac{(-1)^{n-1}\,(-2)^n}{2^n\,n^2} \quad \text{or} \quad \sum \frac{(-1)}{n^2} \quad \text{or} \quad -\sum \frac{1}{n^2} \quad \text{and}$$

$$\sum \frac{(-1)^{n-1}\,2^n}{2^n\,n^2} = \sum \frac{(-1)^{n-1}}{n^2} \quad \text{Both the series are abso-}$$

lutely convergent by the p-series test.

$\therefore$ the interval of convergence of the given series is $-4 \leqslant x \leqslant 0$.

If a power series converges for certain values of x, we may define the series as a function of x.

The set of values of x for which the power series is convergent is the domain and the actual values of the power series for those values of x which make it convergent form the range of the function. Thus we may write

$$f(x) = \sum_{n=0}^{\infty} a_n x^n.$$

Now we deal with three special power series, which represent well known functions in Algebra and Calculus.

11.2. Binomial series.

Consider the power series $1 + px + \dfrac{p(p-1)}{2!}\,x^2 + \dots.$

$$+ \frac{p(p-1)\,\dots\,(p-n+1)\,x^n}{n!} + \dots.$$

Here $u_{n+1} = \dfrac{p(p-1)\,\dots\,(p-n)x^{n+1}}{n+1!}$, leaving the first term 1 out of consideration.

Now $\displaystyle\lim_{n \to \infty} \left| \frac{u_{n+1}}{u_n} \right| = \lim \left| \frac{p(p-1)\,\dots\,(p-n)}{n+1!} \right.$

$$\left. \times \frac{n!}{p(p-1)\dots(p-n+1)} \right| x$$

$$= \lim \left| \frac{p-n}{n+1} \right| \cdot |x| = \left| \frac{n-p}{n+1} \right| \cdot |x|$$

$$\equiv \lim \left| \frac{1-\dfrac{p}{n}}{1+\dfrac{1}{n}} \right| \cdot |x| = |x| \text{ as } n \to \infty$$

∴ the series is absolutely convergent when $|x| < 1$ i.e. when $-1 < x < 1$.

When p is a positive integer, the series comes to an end after $p+1$ terms. Then it is no longer an infinite series. The problem of its convergence or divergence arises only when p is negative or a fraction. When $|x| < 1$, the series is convergent as we have proved above. We can assign a function to the series when p is negative or a fraction and $|x| < 1$. We may define this power series as $(1+x)^p$, which is already the case when p is a positive integer. Actually you will learn in Calculus the reverse operation, viz. to expand a given function into a power series known as Maclaurin's series. Then you will prove that $(1+x)^p = 1 + p \cdot x + \dfrac{p(p-1)}{2} x^2 + \ldots.$

$\ldots. + \dfrac{p(p-1)(p-2) \ldots \ldots (p-n+1)}{n} x^n \ldots \ldots$ where p is any rational number, i.e. a positive integer, a negative integer or a fraction and $|x| < 1$.

Example 1: Find the first 5 terms of the series in the expansion of $(1+x)^{\frac{2}{3}}$.

$$(1+x)^{\frac{2}{3}} = 1 + \tfrac{2}{3}x + \frac{\tfrac{2}{3}(-\tfrac{1}{3})x^2}{2!} + \frac{\tfrac{2}{3}(-\tfrac{1}{3})(-\tfrac{4}{3})\, x^3}{3!}$$

$$+ \frac{\tfrac{2}{3}(-\tfrac{1}{3})(-\tfrac{4}{3})(-\tfrac{7}{3})\, x^4}{4!} + \ldots \ldots$$

$$= 1 + \tfrac{2}{3}x - \tfrac{1}{9}x^2 + \tfrac{4}{81}x^3 - \tfrac{7}{243}x^4 + \ldots \ldots$$

Example 2: Expand $(1-x)^{-1}$.

$$(1-x)^{-1} = 1 + x + \frac{(-1)(-2)}{2!} x^2 + \frac{(-1)(-2)(-3)(-x)^3}{3!}$$
$$+ \ldots\ldots = 1 + x + x^2 + x^3 + x^4 + \ldots\ldots\ldots$$

This is an infinite geometric series convergent for $-1 < x < 1$.

11.3. The exponential series.

Consider the series $1 + x + \frac{x^2}{2!} + \frac{x^3}{3!} + \ldots + \frac{x^n}{n!} + \ldots\ldots$

Leaving the first term 1 out of consideration,

$$u_{n+1} = \frac{x^{n+1}}{n+1!} \text{ and } u_n = \frac{x^n}{n!}$$

$$\therefore \left| \frac{u_{n+1}}{u_n} \right| = \lim \left| \frac{x^{n+1}}{n+1!} \cdot \frac{n!}{x^n} \right| = \lim \left| \frac{x}{n+1} \right| \text{ as } n \to \infty.$$

Now $\lim \left| \frac{x}{n+1} \right| \to 0$ as $n \to \infty$, whatever be the value of x.
$\therefore$ the series is absolutely convergent for all values of x such that $-\infty < x < \infty$.

We can define this series also as a function. We call it e^x.
Later on you will learn $e^x = 1 + x + \frac{x^2}{2!} + \frac{x^3}{3!} + \ldots\ldots$ by Maclaurin's series, where e is a number between 2 and 3 (vide p. 150)

More generally we have $e^{kx} = 1 + kx + \frac{k^2x^2}{2!} + \frac{k^3x^3}{3!} + \ldots$

11.4. The logarithmic series.

Consider the series

$$x - \frac{x^2}{2} + \frac{x^3}{3} - \ldots\ldots + (-1)^{n-1}\frac{x^n}{n} + \ldots$$

Here $u_n = (-1)^{n-1}\frac{x^n}{n}$ and $u_{n+1} = \frac{(-1)^n x^{n+1}}{n+1}$.

$$\therefore \left| \frac{u_{n+1}}{u_n} \right| = \left| -x \cdot \frac{n}{n+1} \right| = |x| \cdot \left| \frac{n}{n+1} \right|$$

$$\therefore \lim \left| \frac{u_{n+1}}{u_n} \right| = \lim \left| \frac{n}{n+1} \right| \cdot |x| = |x| \text{ as}$$

$$\left| \frac{n}{n+1} \right| \to 1 \text{ as } n \to \infty$$

$\therefore$ the series is absolutely convergent if $-1 < x < 1$. When $x=1$, the series will be $1-\frac{1}{2}+\frac{1}{3}-\frac{1}{4}+ \ldots$ which is already known to be convergent.

When $x=-1$, the series will be $-(1+\frac{1}{2}+\frac{1}{3}+\frac{1}{4}+ \ldots)$ which is also shown to be divergent (vide discussions of the p—series.)

$\therefore$ this series is absolutely convergent for $-1 < x \leqslant 1$. This series is defined as $\log_e (1+x)$ or $\log (1+x)$ and when you expand this function into Maclaurin's series, you will obtain exactly the same series as the one we have been considering.

$$\therefore \log (1+x) = x - \frac{x^2}{2} + \frac{x^3}{3} - \frac{x^4}{4} + \ldots \ldots \text{ for } -1 < x \leqslant 1$$

Example 3: Show that $\dfrac{e^x+e^{-x}}{2} = 1 + \dfrac{x^2}{2!} + \dfrac{x^4}{4!} + \ldots + \dfrac{x^{2n}}{2n!} + \ldots$

Since the two series e^x and e^{-x} are absolutely convergent, they can be added up term by term.

$$e^x = 1 + x + \frac{x^2}{2!} + \frac{x^3}{3!} + \ldots$$

$$\text{and } e^{-x} = 1 - x + \frac{x^2}{2!} - \frac{x^3}{3!} + \frac{x^4}{4!} \ldots \ldots$$

$$\therefore e^x + e^{-x} = 2\left(1 + \frac{x^2}{2!} + \frac{x^4}{4!} + \ldots \right) \text{ and}$$

$$\frac{e^x + e^{-x}}{2} = 1 + \frac{x^2}{2!} + \frac{x^4}{4!} + \ldots \ldots$$

Example 4 : Obtain the expansion of $\log \dfrac{1+x}{1-x}$.

$$\log (1+x) = x - \frac{x^2}{2} + \frac{x^3}{3} + \frac{x^4}{4} + \cdots\cdots$$

$$\log (1-x) = -x - \frac{x^2}{2} - \frac{x^3}{3} - \frac{x^4}{4} - \cdots\cdots$$

Both are absolutely convergent in the interval $-1 < x < 1$. Notice that second series is not convergent for $x=1$. Nor is $\log 0$ defined. Hence $x=1$ is to be left out while combining the two series.

$$\therefore \log (1+x) - \log (1-x)$$
$$= \log \frac{1+x}{1-x} = 2\left(x + \frac{x^3}{3} + \frac{x^5}{5} + \cdots\cdots\right)$$

Corollary : $\log \dfrac{m}{n} = 2\left[\dfrac{m-n}{m+n} + \dfrac{1}{3}\left(\dfrac{m-n}{m+n}\right)^3 + \cdots\cdots\right]$

If we put $x = \dfrac{m-n}{m+n}$ in $\log \dfrac{1+x}{1-x}$ we obtain the result.

This result is useful in calculating the logarithms to base e of 2, 3, 4, etc.

If $m=2$, $n=1$, we have $\dfrac{m-n}{m+n} = \frac{1}{3}$

$$\therefore \log \frac{m}{n} = \log 2 = 2\left[\frac{1}{3} + \frac{1}{3}\cdot\frac{1}{3^3} + \frac{1}{5}\cdot\frac{1}{5^5} + \cdots\right]$$
$$= 2[\tfrac{1}{3} + \tfrac{1}{81} + {}_{12}\tfrac{1}{215} + \cdots.] \text{ to three terms}$$
$$= 2\,\{0\cdot3333 + 0\cdot0123 + 0\cdot0008\}$$
$$\qquad\qquad\qquad\qquad \text{approximately}$$
$$= 2(0\cdot3464)$$
$$= 0\cdot6928 \text{ or } 0\cdot693 \text{ roughly.}$$

Having found $\log 2$, we can find approximately $\log 3$ by putting $m=3$, $n=2$ and so on. The relation between $\log_e m$ and $\log_{10} m$ is $\log_{10} m = \dfrac{\log_e m}{\log_e 10}$

This result enables us to find approximate values of $\log_{10} 2$, $\log_{10} 3$, etc.

Also $\log_e 2 = 1 - \frac{1}{2} + \frac{1}{3} - \frac{1}{4} + \ldots \ldots$ Although this is a neat result, it does not give good approximation unless we take a large number of terms.

Since $a^x = e^{x \log a}$ where $a > 1$,

the expansion of a^x is $1 + x \log a + \frac{x^2}{2!} (\log a)^2 + \ldots \ldots$

$$+ \ldots \ldots \frac{x^n}{n!} (\log a)^n + \ldots \ldots \ldots, \text{ for,}$$

$$e^{kx} = 1 + kx + \frac{k^2 x^2}{2} + \frac{k^3 x^3}{3} + \ldots \ldots \text{ etc.}$$

where $k = \log_e a$.

Example 5: Find the coefficient of x^n in the expansion of $\log (1 + x + x^2 + x^3)$ in ascending powers of x.

$$\log (1 + x + x^2 + x^3) = \log \left(\frac{1 - x^4}{1 - x} \right) = \log (1 - x)^4 - \log (1 - x)$$

$$= - \left[x^4 + \frac{x^8}{2} + \frac{x^{12}}{3} + \ldots \ldots + \frac{x^{4n}}{n} + \ldots \ldots \right]$$

$$+ \left[1 + x + \frac{x^2}{2} + \ldots \ldots + \frac{x^n}{n} + \ldots \ldots \right]$$

The first term contributes a term in x^n, if n is a multiple of 4 only.   Otherwise, the coefficient of x^n is $\frac{1}{n}$ only from the second series.

If $n = 4k$, where k is any integer,

the term containing x^n in the first series is $- \frac{x^{4k}}{k}$

where $k = \frac{n}{4}$.

∴ the coefficient of x^n in log $(1+x+x^2+x^3)$, if n is a multiple of 4,

$$= -\frac{4}{n} + \frac{1}{n} = -\frac{3}{n}.$$

If n is not a multiple of 4, the coefficient of x^n is $\frac{1}{n}$.

Example 6 : Sum the series $\dfrac{1}{1 \cdot 2} + \dfrac{1}{3 \cdot 4} + \dfrac{1}{5 \cdot 6} + \ldots$

The given series $= (1 - \frac{1}{2}) + (\frac{1}{3} - \frac{1}{4}) + (\frac{1}{5} - \frac{1}{6}) + \ldots$
$$= 1 - \tfrac{1}{2} + \tfrac{1}{3} - \tfrac{1}{4} + \tfrac{1}{5} - \tfrac{1}{6} + \ldots$$
$$= \log (1+x) \text{ when } x=1$$
$$= \log 2. \quad (\because \text{ the expansion is valid when } x=1)$$

Example 7 : Prove that $\log_2 e - \log_4 e + \log_8 e - \log_{16} e + \ldots = 1$

By changing the base to e, we have $\log_2 e = \dfrac{\log_e e}{\log_e 2} = \dfrac{1}{\log 2}$.

Similarly, $\log_4 e = \dfrac{1}{\log_e 4} = \dfrac{1}{2 \log_e 2}$ etc.

The given series is
$$\frac{1}{\log 2} - \frac{1}{\log 2^2} + \frac{1}{\log 2^3} - \frac{1}{\log 2^4} + \ldots$$
$$= \frac{1}{\log 2} - \frac{1}{2 \log 2} + \frac{1}{3 \log 2} - \frac{1}{4 \log 2} + \ldots$$
$$= \frac{1}{\log 2} \cdot \left[1 - \frac{1}{2} + \frac{1}{3} - \frac{1}{4} + \ldots \right]$$
$$= \frac{1}{\log 2} \times \log 2 = 1.$$

Example 8 : Sum the series
$$1 + \frac{1+2}{2!} + \frac{1+2+3}{3!} + \frac{1+2+3+4}{4!} + \ldots$$

$$u_n = \frac{n(n+1)}{2n!} = \frac{n+1}{2(n-1)!} = \frac{n-1+2}{2(n-1)!}$$

$$= \frac{1}{2(n-2)!} + \frac{1}{(n-1)!}$$

$$S = \tfrac{1}{2} \sum \frac{1}{n-2!} + \sum \frac{1}{n-1!}$$

$$= \tfrac{1}{2} \left[1 + \frac{1}{1!} + \frac{1}{2!} + \frac{1}{3!} + \ldots \right] + \left[1 + \frac{1}{1!} + \frac{1}{2!} + \ldots \right]$$

$$= \tfrac{1}{2}e + e$$

$$= \tfrac{3}{2}e.$$

Note that $-1!$ has no meaning and $0! = 1$ by definition
The first series begins only when $n = 2$.

Example 9: Find the sum of $\sum\limits_{n-1}^{\infty} \frac{(n^2+n)x^n}{n!}$.

$$\frac{n^2+n}{n!} = \frac{n^2}{n!} + \frac{n}{n!} = \frac{n}{n-1!} + \frac{1}{n-1!} = \frac{n-1+1}{n-1!} + \frac{1}{n-1!}$$

$$= \frac{1}{(n-1)!} + \frac{1}{(n-2)!} + \frac{1}{(n-1)!}$$

$$= \frac{1}{(n-2)!} + \frac{2}{(n-1)!}$$

The given series is $x^2 \sum \frac{x^{n-2}}{n-2!} + 2x \sum \frac{x^{n-1}}{n-1!}$ where the summation is from $n=2$ in the first series and from $n=1$ in the second series to infinity.

The series $= x^2 e^x + 2x e^x$
$$= e^x(x^2 + 2x).$$

Exercise 11.1

Find the interval of absolute convergence for the series:

1. $\sum\limits_{1}^{\infty} nx^{n-1}$.

2. $\sum\limits_{n=0}^{\infty} \frac{x^n}{n+1}$.

3. $\sum\limits_{n=1}^{\infty} n^2 x^n.$

4. $\sum\limits_{n=0}^{\infty} \dfrac{(-1)^n x^n}{n!}.$

5. $\sum\limits_{n=0}^{\infty} (2x)^n.$

6. $\sum\limits_{n=1}^{\infty} \dfrac{nx^n}{2^n}.$

7. $\sum\limits_{n=0}^{\infty} (-1)^n (n+1) x^n.$

8. $\sum\limits_{n=1}^{\infty} \dfrac{x^n}{2^n n^3}.$

9. $\sum\limits_{n=1}^{\infty} (-1)^{n-1} \dfrac{(x-1)^n}{n}.$

10. $\sum\limits_{n=1}^{\infty} \dfrac{n^2}{2^n} (x+2)^n.$

11. $\sum\limits_{n=1}^{\infty} \dfrac{(x+2)^n}{\sqrt{n}}.$

12. $\sum\limits_{n=0}^{\infty} \dfrac{(-1)^n x^n}{5^n}.$

13. $\sum\limits_{n=1}^{\infty} \dfrac{x^n}{n}.$

14. $\sum\limits_{n=1}^{\infty} \dfrac{x^n}{(2n-1)(2n)}.$

15. $\sum\limits_{n=1}^{\infty} \dfrac{x^{n-1}}{n^2}.$

Expand the following functions:

16. $(1+x)^{-2}.$

17. $(1-x)^{-2}.$

18. $(1+x)^{-3}.$

19. $(1-x)^{-3}.$

Find the $n+1$th term in the expansion of

20. $(1-x)^{-4}.$

21. $(1+2x)^{\frac{1}{2}}.$

22. $(2-x)^{-2}.$

23. $(1-x)^{-\frac{1}{2}}.$

24. If x is large and positive, show that

$$(1+x^3)^{\frac{1}{3}} = x + \frac{1}{3x^2} - \frac{1}{9x^5} \text{ correct up to } \frac{1}{x^5}.$$

25. If $x > \frac{1}{2}$ prove that

$$x^n = 1 + n\left(1 - \frac{1}{x}\right) + \frac{n(n+1)}{2!}\left(1 - \frac{1}{x}\right)^2 + \cdots$$

Find the sum of the following series:

26. $1 + \dfrac{2}{3} \cdot \dfrac{1}{2} + \dfrac{2 \cdot 5}{3 \cdot 6} \dfrac{1}{2^2} + \dfrac{2 \cdot 5 \cdot 8}{3 \cdot 6 \cdot 9} \dfrac{1}{2^3} + \cdots$

27. $1 + \dfrac{4}{6} + \dfrac{4 \cdot 5}{6 \cdot 9} + \dfrac{4 \cdot 5 \cdot 6}{6 \cdot 9 \cdot 12} + \ldots\ldots$

28. $1 + \dfrac{3}{4} + \dfrac{3 \cdot 5}{4 \cdot 8} + \dfrac{3 \cdot 5 \cdot 7}{4 \cdot 8 \cdot 12} + \ldots\ldots$

29. $1 - \dfrac{1}{2} \cdot \dfrac{1}{2} + \dfrac{1 \cdot 3}{2 \cdot 4} \cdot \dfrac{1}{2^2} - \dfrac{1 \cdot 3 \cdot 5}{2 \cdot 4 \cdot 6} \dfrac{1}{2^3} + \ldots\ldots$

30. $1 + \dfrac{5}{8} + \dfrac{5.7}{8 \cdot 12} + \dfrac{5 \cdot 7 \cdot 9}{8 \cdot 12 \cdot 16} + \ldots\ldots$

31. Prove that $\dfrac{e^x - e^{-x}}{2} = 1 + \dfrac{x^3}{3!} + \dfrac{x^5}{5!} + \ldots\ldots + \dfrac{x^{2n-1}}{(2n-1)!} + \ldots$

and hence find the sum of the infinite series

$$1 + \dfrac{1}{3!} + \dfrac{1}{5!} + \ldots\ldots$$

32. Show that $\left(1 + \dfrac{1}{2!} + \dfrac{1}{4!} + \ldots\ldots\right)^2$

$$= 1 + \left(1 + \dfrac{1}{3!} + \dfrac{1}{5!} + \ldots\ldots\right)^2$$

33. Prove that $\dfrac{1}{3!} + \dfrac{2}{5!} + \dfrac{3}{7!} + \ldots\ldots = \dfrac{1}{2e}$.

34. Prove that $\dfrac{2}{3!} + \dfrac{4}{5!} + \dfrac{6}{7!} + \ldots\ldots = \dfrac{1}{e}$.

35. Prove that $\dfrac{1^2}{1!} + \dfrac{2^2}{2!} + \dfrac{3^2}{3!} + \ldots\ldots = 2e$

36. Prove that $\log(1 + 3x + 2x^2) = 3x - \dfrac{5x^2}{2} + \dfrac{9x^3}{3} - \dfrac{17x^4}{4}\ldots\ldots$

Find the interval of convergence for this series

37. Find the coefficient of x^n in the expansion of $\log(1 + x + x^2)$.

38. If $y = x - \dfrac{x^2}{2} + \dfrac{x^3}{3} - \dfrac{x^4}{4} + \ldots\ldots$ show that

$$x = y + \dfrac{y^2}{2!} + \dfrac{y^3}{3!} + \dfrac{y^4}{4!} + \ldots\ldots$$

For what values of x and y is this result true?

39. Show that $\log \dfrac{x}{y} = \dfrac{x-y}{x} - \dfrac{1}{2} \left(\dfrac{x-y}{x}\right)^2 + \dfrac{1}{3} \left(\dfrac{x-y}{x}\right)^3 - \ldots\ldots$

40. Find the sum of the series $\dfrac{1}{1\cdot2} - \dfrac{1}{2\cdot3} + \dfrac{1}{3\cdot4} - \dfrac{1}{4\cdot5} + \ldots\ldots$

41. Prove that $\dfrac{1}{1\cdot3} + \dfrac{1}{2\cdot5} + \dfrac{1}{3\cdot7} + \dfrac{1}{4\cdot9} + \ldots\ldots = 2\,(1-\log 2)$

ANSWERS

CHAPTER 1

Exercise 1

1. $A' = \{2, 3, 4\}$.

2. $A \cup B = \{a, b, c, 3, 5\}$, $A \cap B = \{a\}$.

3. (i) $\{1, 2\}$, (ii) $\{1\}$, $\{2\}$, (iii) ϕ, four.

4. $\{a, b, c\}$, $\{a, b\}$, $\{b, c\}$, $\{c, a\}$, $\{a\}$, $\{b\}$, $\{c\}$, ϕ.
    (ii) 8 (iii) A set containing n elements has 2^n subsets.

5. $A = \{1, 2, 3, 4\}$ $B = \{5, 6, \ldots\ldots\}$,
    $A \cup B = N$ and $A \cap B = \phi$.

6. (i) 12, (ii) 12, (iii) 16.

7. $\{(-3, -3), (-3, 2), (-3, 4), (2, -3), (2, 2), (2, 4), (4, -3), (4, 2), (4, 4)\}$.

10. (i) A and B have no common elements, either $A = \phi$ or $B = \phi$ or both A and B are ϕ.
    (ii) $A = \phi$, $B = \phi$, (iii) $A = U$, $B = U$
    (iv) $B = A'$ or $A = B'$ or $A = U$ or $B = U$ or both $A = B = U$,
    (v) $A \subset U$, (vi) $A = \phi$.

11. True.   **12.** False.

13. True.   **14.** True.

15. True.   **16.** True.

17. True.   **18.** False.

19. 29.   **20.** $n(A \cap B) = 4$, $n(A) - n(B) = 6$.

CHAPTER 3

Exercise 3.2

1. $\{x \mid x \geqslant -3\}$.   **2.** $\{x \mid x \leqslant -2\}$.

3. $\{x \mid x \leqslant 3\}$.   **4.** $\{x \mid x < 3\}$.

5. $\{x \mid x \geqslant 2\}$.   **6.** $\{x \mid x > \frac{1}{3}\}$.

7. $\{x \mid x > -\frac{1}{3}\}$.   **8.** $\{x \mid x > -12\}$.

9. $\{x \mid x \leqslant 1\}$.   **10.** $\{x \mid x \geqslant -3\frac{1}{5}\}$.

11. $\{x \mid x > 2 \text{ or } < -2\}$.   **12.** $\{x \mid -\frac{3}{2} \leqslant x \leqslant \frac{3}{2}\}$.

13. $\{x \mid x < 3 \text{ or } > 4\}$.   **14.** $\{x \mid 2 \leqslant x \leqslant 3\}$.

15. $\{x \mid x < 3 \text{ or } > 4\}$.   **16.** $\{x \mid 2 > x > -3\}$.

17. $\{x \mid 1 \leqslant x \leqslant 2$.   **18.** $\{x \mid -7 \geqslant x \geqslant 12\}$.

19. $\{x \mid x < -1,\ 3 < x < 4\}$.   **20.** $\{x \mid x \geqslant 1,\ -3 \geqslant x \geqslant -4\}$.

Exercise 3.3

11. $\sqrt{3} + \sqrt{5}$.   **12.** $\sqrt{\frac{4}{9}} + \sqrt{\frac{2}{5}}$.

CHAPTER 4

1. Function.   **2.** Function.   **3.** Function.

4. Function.   **5.** Relation.   **6.** Relation.

7. Function.   **8.** Function.   **9.** Function.

10. Relation.

CHAPTER 5

Exercise 5.1

1. $(-1, 2)$.   **2.** $(-5, 8)$.   **3.** $(13, -1)$.

4. $(12, 11)$.   **5.** $(2, -1)$.   **6.** $(8, 8)$.

7. $(-2, 4)$.   **8.** $(0, 0)$.   **9.** $(1\frac{2}{5}, \frac{1}{5})$.

10. $(1\frac{2}{13}, -\frac{5}{13})$.   **11.** $(2\frac{9}{13}, 2\frac{4}{13})$.   **15.** $\left(\dfrac{x}{x^2+y^2}, \dfrac{-y}{x^2+y^2}\right)$; $(\frac{2}{5}, \frac{1}{5})$.

Exercise 5.2

1. $5 - 2i$.   **2.** $8 + 10i$.   **3.** $2 + 2i$.

4. $-2 + 6i$.   **5.** $30 - 15i$.   **6.** $1 + 3i$.

7. 25.   **8.** $(6 + \sqrt{2}) + (3\sqrt{2} - 2)i$.

9. $12 - \sqrt{3}i$.   **11.** $20 + 10\sqrt{5}i$.   **12.** $17 - 9\sqrt{2}i$.

13. $-1 - 8\sqrt{2}i$,   **14.** $-1 - 2\sqrt{2}i$.   **15.** $-8i$.

16. $-8i$.   **17.** $\frac{3}{13} - \frac{2}{13}i$.   **18.** $-\dfrac{i}{2}$.

19. $-\dfrac{5}{29}-\dfrac{2i}{29}$. **20.** $\frac{1}{11}(3+\sqrt{2}i)$. **21.** $\frac{1}{196}(1+4\sqrt{3}i)$.

22. $\frac{1}{2}(1+5i)$. **23.** $\frac{1}{13}(-5+14i)$. **24.** $\frac{1}{2}(5-3i)$.

25. $-i$. **26.** $-i$. **27.** i.

28. $\frac{1}{13}(29-11i)$. **29.** -1.

30. $\dfrac{-(41+12\sqrt{5}i)}{49}$. **32.** $x-3, y=\dfrac{4}{5}$.

33. $x=-\dfrac{2}{3}; y=-12$. **34.** $x=\dfrac{2}{5}, y=-\dfrac{1}{5}$.

35. $x=-\dfrac{2}{9}, y=\dfrac{1}{3}$.

Exercise 5.3

1. $\sqrt{2}$. **2.** $\sqrt{2}$. **3.** 2.

4. 13. **5.** $\sqrt{41}$. **6.** $4\sqrt{2}$.

7. 1. **8.** $\dfrac{\sqrt{13}}{5}$. **9.** $\dfrac{5}{2}$.

20. $\sqrt{17}\,(\cos\theta+i\sin\theta)$ where $\cos\theta=\dfrac{1}{\sqrt{17}}$;

$\sin\theta=\dfrac{4}{\sqrt{17}}$;

$\sqrt{17}\,(\cos\theta+i\sin\theta)$ where $\cos\theta=\dfrac{1}{\sqrt{17}}$, $\sin\theta=-\dfrac{4}{\sqrt{17}}$;

$\cos 120°+i\sin 120°$; $\cos 240°+i\sin 240°$.

CHAPTER 6

1. 9. **2.** 12. **3.** 15. **4.** 1.

5. 34. **6.** 13. **7.** 21 **8.** 29.

9. 35. **10.** 6. **11.** $k=-2$ and $l=3$

12. H.C.F.$=15$, $k=-2$ and $l=3$.

13. H.C.F.$=13$, $k=4$ and $l=-3$.

14. $k=13$ and $l=-43$.

15. H.C.F. is 33, $k=8$ and $l=-13$.

CHAPTER 7

Exercise 7.1

1. 10.	**2.** 17.	**3.** 0.	**4.** -25.
5. 500.	**6.** -25.	**7.** $5\frac{5}{16}$.	**8.** $2\frac{46}{81}$.
9. -6.	**10.** 0.	**11.** yes.	**12.** yes.
13. yes.	**14.** no.	**15.** no.	**16.** yes.
17. no.	**18.** no.	**19.** no.	**20.** no; yes.

Exercise 7.2

1. $x+2$.   **2.** $x+1$.   **3.** $x-2$.

4. x^2+1.   **5.** x^2+x+1.   **6.** x^2-x+1.

7. $\phi(x)=\dfrac{1}{5}$ and $\psi(x)=-\dfrac{1}{5}$.

8. $\phi(x)=\dfrac{1}{2}$ and $\psi(x)=-\dfrac{1}{2}(x+1)$.

9. H.C.F.$=x^2+3$,
$$\phi(x)=\frac{-4}{19} \text{ and } \psi(x)=-\frac{(2x-3)}{19}.$$

Exercise 7.3

1. $(-2, -3, 5)$.   **2.** $(4, 4, -5)$.

3. $(-1, 2, 3)$.   **4.** $(-2, -1 \pm i\sqrt{3})$.

5. $(1, -2, \pm 6)$.   **6.** $(1, -1, -2, 3)$.

7. $(2, 3, -3, -4)$.   **8.** $(2, -2, -\frac{1}{2}\pm i\sqrt{35})$.

9. $\left(2, 2, -\frac{1}{2}\pm\dfrac{i\sqrt{3}}{2}\right)$.   **10.** $(1, 2, 3, -5)$.

11. $\left(\frac{1}{2}, \dfrac{-3\pm\sqrt{5}}{2}\right)$.   **12.** $\left(4, \pm\dfrac{1}{\sqrt{2}}\right)$.

13. $\left(-2, 3, \dfrac{1}{2}\right)$.   **14.** $\left(\dfrac{1}{3}, \dfrac{3}{2}, \dfrac{5}{2}\right)$.

15. $\left(\dfrac{-1}{2}, \dfrac{-1}{2}, \dfrac{1\pm\sqrt{5}}{2}\right)$.   **16.** $\left(\dfrac{3}{2}, \dfrac{3}{2}, \pm i\right)$.

17. $\left(2, -\dfrac{3}{2}, \pm 2i\right).$ **18.** $\left(\dfrac{1}{2}, \dfrac{1}{2}, \pm\sqrt{3}\right).$

19. $\left(-\dfrac{1}{3}, \dfrac{5}{2}, \sqrt{3}, -\sqrt{3}\right).$

20. $\left(-\dfrac{3}{2}, -\dfrac{2}{3}, -1\pm\sqrt{2}\,i\right).$

21. $\left(-2, 4, \dfrac{-1\pm\sqrt{11i}}{2}\right).$

22. $\left(-1, \tfrac{3}{2}, \dfrac{-1+\sqrt{3i}}{2}\right).$

23. $\left(-\dfrac{3}{2}, -\dfrac{3}{2}, \dfrac{1\pm\sqrt{5}}{2}\right).$

24. $\left(\dfrac{1}{2}, \dfrac{1}{2}, 3, \pm i\right).$

25. $\left(\pm 1, \pm 2i, -\dfrac{2}{3}\right).$

Exercise 7.5

1. sum $= -\tfrac{1}{2}$, product $= 2$.   **2.** $-1, 1, 3$.

3. $-3, -1, 2; k = -5$.   **4.** $k = 12; 3, -2$.

5. $3, 2, -3, -2; a = b = 0$.   **6.** $l = -7, k = -6; -2, -1, 3$.

10. $h = 10, k = 8; -\tfrac{1}{2}, 2, 4$.

11. $3\tfrac{7}{9}$.   **12.** $5\tfrac{5}{16}$.

CHAPTER 8

Exercise 8.1

1. $\begin{bmatrix} 2 & 11 \\ 1 & 2 \end{bmatrix}.$ **2.** $A = \begin{bmatrix} 1 & 3 & 4 \\ 4 & 10 & -2 \end{bmatrix}.$

3. $A = \begin{bmatrix} 4 & 7 \\ 2 & 10 \end{bmatrix}.$ **4.** $A = \begin{bmatrix} \dfrac{9}{2} & -1 & \dfrac{11}{2} \\ -4 & 1 & 3 \end{bmatrix}.$

5. $A = \begin{bmatrix} -17 & -24 \\ -1 & 35 \end{bmatrix}.$

6. $A = \begin{bmatrix} 2 & -\dfrac{3}{2} & 1 \\ -2 & 0 & -2 \end{bmatrix}.$

7. $A = \begin{bmatrix} 5 & 1 & 9 \\ 9 & 1 & 7 \\ \dfrac{9}{2} & 1 & 7 \end{bmatrix}.$

8. $A = \begin{bmatrix} 1 & 4 \\ 1 & 1 \end{bmatrix}.$

9. $B = \begin{bmatrix} 1 & -1 \\ 2 & -2 \end{bmatrix},$ $\qquad A = \begin{bmatrix} 4 & 1 \\ 3 & -3 \end{bmatrix}.$

10. $A = \begin{bmatrix} 2 & 3 \\ 2 & 2 \end{bmatrix},$ $\qquad B = \begin{bmatrix} -1 & -2 \\ 1 & 0 \end{bmatrix}$

11. $B = \begin{bmatrix} 3 & 0 & 1 \\ 0 & -2 & 3 \end{bmatrix},$ $\qquad A = \begin{bmatrix} -4 & 1 & -2 \\ 1 & 3 & -4 \end{bmatrix}.$

12. $A = \begin{bmatrix} 2 & -1 & 1 \\ 1 & 2 & 0 \end{bmatrix},$ $\qquad B = \begin{bmatrix} 1 & 1 & 2 \\ -1 & 1 & -2 \end{bmatrix}.$

13. $AB = \begin{bmatrix} 7 & 9 \\ 8 & 11 \end{bmatrix},$ $\qquad BA = \begin{bmatrix} 5 & 5 \\ 12 & 13 \end{bmatrix}.$

14. $AB = \begin{bmatrix} 2 & -8 \\ 24 & 14 \end{bmatrix},$ $\qquad BA = \begin{bmatrix} 2 & -12 \\ 16 & 14 \end{bmatrix}.$

15. $AB = \begin{bmatrix} 14 & 19 \\ 2 & 5 \end{bmatrix},$ $\qquad BA = \begin{bmatrix} 21 & -2 \\ 37 & -2 \end{bmatrix}.$

16. $AB = \begin{bmatrix} 60 & -60 \\ 84 & -72 \end{bmatrix}$ $\qquad BA = \begin{bmatrix} 30 & 66 \\ -30 & -42 \end{bmatrix}.$

17. $AB = \begin{bmatrix} -10 & 8 \\ -66 & -32 \end{bmatrix},$ $\quad BA = \begin{bmatrix} 31 & 51 \\ -61 & -73 \end{bmatrix}.$

18. $AB = \begin{bmatrix} 8 & 10 \\ -4 & 10 \end{bmatrix},$ $\quad BA = \begin{bmatrix} 0 & 2 & 14 \\ -6 & 2 & 2 \\ -6 & 4 & 16 \end{bmatrix}.$

19. $AB = \begin{bmatrix} 6 & 7 & -2 \\ -8 & -6 & -3 \end{bmatrix},$ $\quad BA$ is not defined.

20. $AB = BA = B = \begin{bmatrix} 1 & 2 & 3 \\ 2 & 3 & 4 \\ 3 & 4 & 5 \end{bmatrix}.$

21. $AB = BA = B = \begin{bmatrix} 2 & 0 & 0 \\ 0 & 2 & 0 \\ 0 & 0 & 2 \end{bmatrix}.$

22. $AB = \begin{bmatrix} 0 & 0 & 0 \\ 0 & 0 & 0 \\ 0 & 0 & 0 \end{bmatrix}, \qquad BA = \begin{bmatrix} 0 & 0 & 0 \\ 0 & 0 & 0 \\ 1 & 1 & 0 \end{bmatrix}.$

24. $\begin{bmatrix} 5 & 1 & -1 \\ 4 & 2 & -2 \\ 2 & 3 & 6 \end{bmatrix}$

25. $x=2, y=4.$

26. $x=7, y=16.$

27. $x=3, y=4.$

28. $x=2, y=4, z=14.$

29. $x=(10, 11), y=(-1, -2), z=(5, 1).$

30. $x=(3, -6, 9, 0), y=(4, -8, 12, 0), z=(5, -10, 15, 0).$

31. $\begin{bmatrix} 5 & 5 & 2 \\ 26 & 4 & 10 \\ 25 & 32 & 5 \end{bmatrix}.$

32. $ax^2+by^2+cz^2+2hxy+2gxz+2fyz.$

Exercise 8.2

  1. $-19.$ **2.** $29.$ **3.** $0.$ **4.** $-150.$ **5.** $abc+2fgh-af^2-ch^2-bg^2.$

  6. $-30.$ **7.** $-10.$ **8.** $-29.$ **9.** $0.$

10. $340.$ **11.** $-240.$ **12.** $252.$ **13.** $0.$

14. $-69.$ **15.** $-132.$ **16.** $10.$ **17.** $0.$

Exercise 8.3

  1. $2.$ **2.** $2.$ **3.** $3.$ **4.** $3.$

  5. $2.$ **6.** $2.$ **7.** $2.$ **8.** $3.$

  9. $3.$ **10.** $4.$ **11.** $4.$ **12.** $4.$

13. $2.$ **14.** $4.$

CHAPTER 9

1. $x=1, y=1$. **2.** $x=2, y=-3$.

3. $(-1, 1, 0)$. **4.** $(2, -1, 1)$.

5. $x=11z+13, y=-6z-5$, z is arbitrary.

6. $\left(-\dfrac{7}{58}, \dfrac{3}{29}, \dfrac{1}{29}\right)$. **7.** Inconsistent.

8. $\left(\dfrac{1}{6}, \dfrac{-2}{3}, \dfrac{1}{2}\right)$. **9.** $1, 2, -1$.

10. $x=2+\frac{13}{5}z, y=3-\frac{11}{5}z$, where z is arbitrary.

11. $(2, -4, 7)$.

12. $y=\frac{1}{5}$, $z=x-\frac{13}{5}$ and x is arbitrary.

13. $(6-\frac{5}{3}z, -5+\frac{7}{3}z, z)$.

14. Inconsistent. **15.** $(2, 1, -1, -2)$.

16. $(\frac{53}{68} \frac{85}{68}, \frac{58}{68}, -\frac{1}{68})$. **17.** $(1, -1, 2, \frac{1}{3})$.

18. $(2, -1, \frac{1}{2}, 1)$. **19.** $(-2, 1, -1, 3)$.

20. $z=1, t=2, x=7-2y-3w, y$ and w having any values.

CHAPTER 10

Exercise 10.1

1. Convergent. Limit is $-\frac{1}{2}$.

2. con. limit $\frac{1}{2}$. **3.** con. limit 2.

4. con. limit 2. **5.** div.

6. con. $\frac{1}{2}$. **7.** con. 1.

8. div. **9.** div.

10. con. 0. **11.** div.

12. div. **13.** con. 0.

14. con. 0. **15.** 1000.

21. $\dfrac{35}{99}$. **22.** $\dfrac{123}{999}$.

23. $\dfrac{1356}{999}$. **24.** $\dfrac{1}{1-r}$.

Exercise 10.2

1. div.	**2.** con.	**3.** div.	**4.** con.
5. con.	**6.** div.	**7.** con.	**8.** div.
9. con.	**10.** div.	**11.** con.	**12.** con.
13. div.	**14.** con.	**15.** div.	

16. $\frac{1}{2}+\frac{2}{3}+\frac{3}{4}$; div.

17. $1+\frac{1}{3!}+\frac{1}{5!}$, con.

18. $\frac{1}{2+1}+\frac{1}{2^2+2}+\frac{1}{2^3+3}$, con.

19. $\frac{1}{2!}+\frac{1}{4!}+\frac{1}{6!}$ con.

20. $\frac{1}{2\cdot3}+\frac{1}{3\cdot4}+\frac{1}{4\cdot5}$; con.

21. $\frac{5}{6}+\frac{7}{12}+\frac{9}{20}$; div.

22. $\frac{2}{4}+\frac{6}{11}+\frac{12}{22}$; div.

23. $\frac{1}{1^2+1}+\frac{1}{2^2+1}+\frac{1}{3^2+1}$; con.

24. $\frac{\sqrt{1}}{1^2}+\frac{\sqrt{2}}{2^2}+\frac{\sqrt{3}}{3^2}$; con.

25. $\frac{1^p}{2^q}+\frac{2^p}{3^q}+\frac{3^p}{4^q}$; con. if $q-p>1$; div. if $q-p\leqslant1$.

Exercise 10.3

1. con.	**2.** con.	**3.** div.	**4.** div.	**5.** con.
6. con.	**7.** div.	**8.** con.	**9.** con.	**10.** con.
11. con.	**12.** con.			

CHAPTER 11

1. $-1<x<1$.	**2.** $-1<x<1$.
3. $-1<x<1$.	**4.** $-\infty<x<\infty$.
5. $-\frac{1}{2}<x<\frac{1}{2}$.	**6.** $-2<x<2$.
7. $-1<x<1$.	**8.** $-2\leqslant x\leqslant2$.
9. $0<x<2$.	**10.** $-4<x<0$.
11. $-3<x<-1$.	**12.** $-5<x<5$.

13. $-1 < x < 1$.   **14.** $-1 \leqslant x \leqslant 1$.

15. $-1 \leqslant x \leqslant 1$.   **16.** $1 - 2x + 3x^2 - 4x^3 + \ldots$.

17. $1 + 2x + 3x^2 + 4x^3 + \ldots$.

18. $1 - 3x + 6x^2 - 10x^3 + \ldots$ **19.** $1 + 3x + 6x^2 + 10x^3 + \ldots$

20. $\dfrac{(n+1)\,(n+2)\,(n+3)}{3!} \cdot x^n$

21. $(-1)^{n-1}\ \dfrac{1 \cdot 3 \cdot 5 \ldots (2n-3)}{n!}\ x^n$

22. $\dfrac{(n+1)}{2^{n+2}} \cdot x^n$.

23. $\dfrac{1 \cdot 3 \cdot 5 \ldots\ldots (2n-1)}{n!}\ \left(\dfrac{x}{2}\right)^n$.

26. $2\sqrt{2}$.   **27.** $1\frac{9}{8}$.   **28.** $\sqrt{8}$.

29. $\sqrt{\frac{2}{3}}$.   **30.** $\frac{4}{3}(2^{\frac{3}{2}} - 1)$.   **31.** $\dfrac{e - e^{-1}}{2}$.

37. $-\dfrac{2}{n}$ if n is a multiple of 3; $\dfrac{1}{n}$ in other cases.

38. $-1 < x \leqslant 1$; $y \leqslant \log_e 2$.   **40.** $\log \dfrac{4}{e}$.

Exercise 10.2

1. div.	**2.** con.	**3.** div.	**4.** con.
5. con.	**6.** div.	**7.** con.	**8.** div.
9. con.	**10.** div.	**11.** con.	**12.** con.
13. div.	**14.** con.	**15.** div.	

16. $\frac{1}{2}+\frac{2}{3}+\frac{3}{4}$; div.

17. $1+\frac{1}{3!}+\frac{1}{5!}$, con.

18. $\frac{1}{2+1}+\frac{1}{2^2+2}+\frac{1}{2^2+3}$, con.

19. $\frac{1}{2!}+\frac{1}{4!}+\frac{1}{6!}$ con.

20. $\frac{1}{2\cdot3}+\frac{1}{3\cdot4}+\frac{1}{4\cdot5}$; con.

21. $\frac{5}{6}+\frac{7}{12}+\frac{9}{20}$; div.

22. $\frac{2}{4}+\frac{6}{11}+\frac{1}{2}\frac{2}{2}$; div.

23. $\frac{1}{1^2+1}+\frac{1}{2^2+1}+\frac{1}{3^2+1}$; con.

24. $\frac{\sqrt{1}}{1^2}+\frac{\sqrt{2}}{2^2}+\frac{\sqrt{3}}{3^2}$; con.

25. $\frac{1^p}{2^q}+\frac{2^p}{3^q}+\frac{3^p}{4^q}$; con. if $q-p>1$; div. if $q-p\leqslant 1$.

Exercise 10.3

1. con.	**2.** con.	**3.** div.	**4.** div.	**5.** con.
6. con.	**7.** div.	**8.** con.	**9.** con.	**10.** con.
11. con.	**12.** con.			

CHAPTER 11

1. $-1<x<1$.	**2.** $-1<x<1$.
3. $-1<x<1$.	**4.** $-\infty<x<\infty$.
5. $-\frac{1}{2}<x<\frac{1}{2}$.	**6.** $-2<x<2$.
7. $-1<x<1$.	**8.** $-2\leqslant x\leqslant 2$.
9. $0<x<2$.	**10.** $-4<x<0$.
11. $-3<x<-1$.	**12.** $-5<x<5$.

13. $-1 < x < 1.$ **14.** $-1 \leqslant x \leqslant 1.$

15. $-1 \leqslant x \leqslant 1.$ **16.** $1-2x+3x^2-4x^3+ \dots .$

17. $1+2x+3x^2+4x^3+ \dots .$

18. $1-3x+6x^2-10x^3+ \dots .$ **19.** $1+3x+6x^2+10x^3+ \dots .$

20. $\dfrac{(n+1)\ (n+2)\ (n+3)}{3!} \cdot x^n$

21. $(-1)^{n-1}\ \dfrac{1 \cdot 3 \cdot 5 \dots . (2n-3)}{n!}\ x^n$

22. $\dfrac{(n+1)}{2^{n+2}} \cdot x^n.$

23. $\dfrac{1 \cdot 3 \cdot 5 \dots \dots (2n-1)}{n!}\ \left(\dfrac{x}{2}\right)^n.$

26. $2\sqrt{2}.$ **27.** $\frac{19}{8}.$ **28.** $\sqrt{8}.$

29. $\sqrt{\frac{2}{3}}.$ **30.** $\frac{4}{3}(2^{\frac{3}{2}}-1).$ **31.** $\dfrac{e-e^{-1}}{2}.$

37. $-\dfrac{2}{n}$ if n is a multiple of 3; $\dfrac{1}{n}$ in other cases.

38. $-1 < x \leqslant 1;\ y \leqslant \log_e 2.$ **40.** $\log \dfrac{4}{e}.$